D1596842

Structural Mechanics

Structural Mechanics:
The Behavior of
Plates and Shells

JACK R. VINSON

**Professor and Chairman of Mechanical and Aerospace
Engineering and Professor of Marine Studies
University of Delaware**

A Wiley-Interscience Publication

JOHN WILEY & SONS, New York · London · Sydney · Toronto

Copyright © 1974, by John Wiley & Sons, Inc.

Library of Congress Cataloging in Publication Data:
Vinson, Jack R   1929-
   Structural mechanics.

   "A Wiley-Interscience publication."
   Includes bibliographical references.
   1. Plates (Engineering) 2. Shells (Engineering)
I. Title.

TA660.P6V55 1974   624′.1776   73-19881

ISBN 0-471-90837-1

Printed in the United States of America

10 9 8 7 6 5 4 3 2 1

This book is dedicated
to my wife Trudy
for her encouragement, patience, and inspiration

PREFACE

This book is intended primarily as a teaching text for a one-semester undergraduate course in structural mechanics. It presupposes that the student has already completed one course in the mechanics of materials, although students have taken a course that uses this text concurrently with a first mechanics of materials course.

The text is also intended to be a useful reference book for practicing engineers who for any of various reasons received little undergraduate instruction in the behavior of plates and shells.

Unlike most other undergraduate texts used in follow-on courses to the mechanics of materials, this one deals with continuous structures, that is, plates and shells. There are many good texts, pertaining more to civil engineering and modern building construction, that treat beams and columns of various cross sections under various loadings. This text, on the other hand, provides a course for civil, mechanical, chemical, aeronautical, and ocean engineers who need some knowledge of plates and shells for application to flight structures, underwater structures, land-based vehicles, pressure vessels, piping, chemical process equipment, and new kinds of housing and buildings.

As stated above, it is a teaching text. It is not an encyclopedia of all previous research and solutions that are known. It provides a fundamental approach to an understanding of the mathematical and physical characteristics of structures involving plates and shells, at a level that undergraduate students can understand.

The length of the book has been restricted intentionally in order that the individual instructor can add additional material appropriate to the institution's curriculum, the students desires, or even the instructor's biases. Some problems have been included, and many more can easily be provided by the instructor.

The result hoped for is that the student understands the behavior of plates and shells, can enter his profession and contribute productively, can read and understand the bulk of the voluminous literature in the field, and can continue to study these areas more deeply at the graduate level.

Chapter 1 derives the governing equations of a rectangular plate starting from the equations of elasticity. The student sees clearly what assumptions are made, and their effect. In Chapter 2 some solutions are obtained, using both the Navier and the Levy methods of solution. Chapter 3 introduces the effects of temperature distributions in plates. It also treats in detail the mathematical complexities introduced by nonhomogeneous boundary conditions, which usually result from thermal loadings. Circular plates are treated in Chapter 4, and several examples are given for cases of axially symmetric loading. The derivation of governing equations for the elastic stability of plates is given in Chapter 5, along with considerable discussion of the physical phenomena involved. Chapter 6 treats the theorem of minimum potential energy, and clearly presents the advantages of using energy principles to treat complicated stability problems rather than solving the differential equations of Chapter 5. Cylindrical shells are covered in great detail in Chapter 7, to show lucidly the peculiar characteristics of shells in general, such as the bending boundary layer. Axially symmetric as well as asymmetric problems are treated. A completely general solution for the axially symmetric cylindrical shell is presented for easy use. Membrane theory, inextensional theory, and the Donnell equations are also treated. In Chapter 8 the student is provided the proper equations to use in treating the elastic stability of cylindrical shells under all loadings, and spherical shells under external pressure. Vibrations of plates and shells are not covered, because these are usually treated in a separate course in vibrations. Obviously, the instructor can expand the material as he wishes. Finally, Chapter 9 provides the solutions to many of the problems given in each of the previous chapters.

Appreciation is here expressed to many of my graduate students and undergraduate students who helped to refine the text. Appreciation is also expressed to Dr. Maurice A. Brull, Tel Aviv University, my doctoral advisor, who initially interested me in plates and shells so long ago. Special thanks also go to Dr. Frederick A. Costello, University of Delaware, and Dr. Michael McCormick, U.S. Naval Academy, without whose active support this text might be merely another revision of my class notes.

JACK R. VINSON

Newark, Delaware
August, 1973

CONTENTS

Structural Mechanics

1

DERIVATION OF THE GOVERNING EQUATIONS FOR A RECTANGULAR PLATE

1.1. BASIC EQUATIONS OF ELASTICITY

Sokolnikoff,[1] in his first three chapters, derives in detail the formulation of the governing differential equations of elasticity. This derivation is not repeated here, but rather the equations are presented and then utilized to express certain assumptions systematically in the process of deriving the governing equations for a rectangular plate.

Consider an elastic body of any general shape, and a typical material point in its interior. If one assigns a Cartesian reference frame with axes x, y, and z, shown in Figure 1.1, it is then convenient to assign a rectangular parallelepiped shape to the material point, and designate it as a control element of dimensions dx, dy, and dz, as shown in the Figure. The control element is defined to be infinitesimally small compared to the size of the elastic body, yet infinitely large compared to elements of the molecular structure, in order that the material can be considered a continuum.

On the surfaces of the control element there can exist both normal stresses (those perpendicular to the plane of the face) and shear stresses (those parallel to the plane of the face). On any one face the three stress components comprise a vector, called a surface traction.

It is important to note the sign convention and the meaning of the subscripts for these surface stresses. A stress component on a positive face (i.e., a face whose outer normal is in the direction of the positive axis) is positive when it is in the direction of the positive axis. Conversely, when a stress component is on a negative face of the control element, it is positive when it is in the negative axis direction. This convention is followed in Figure 1.1. Furthermore the first subscript of any stress component signi-

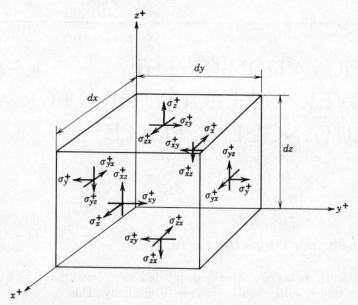

Fig. 1.1. Control element in an elastic body.

fies the axis parallel to the outer normal of the face on which the stress component acts. The second subscript refers to the axis parallel to the stress component. However, it can be shown that $\sigma_{ij} = \sigma_{ji}$. For normal stresses the subscripts are therefore repeated, and often the two subscripts are shortened to one, that is, $\sigma_i = \sigma_{ii}$, where $i = x, y,$ or z.

The u, v, and w displacements are parallel to the x, y, and z axes, respectively, and are positive when in the positive axis direction.

Strains in an elastic body are also of two types, extensional and shear. Extensional strains, ε_{ii}, where $i = x, y,$ or z, are directed parallel to each of the axes and are a measure of the change in dimension of the control volume in the subscripted direction due to the normal stresses acting on all surfaces of the control volume. Looking at Figure 1.2, one can define shear strains.

The shear strain ε_{ij} (where i and $j = x, y,$ or z, and $i \neq j$) is a change of angle. In the example shown in Figure 1.2, in the x-y plane, define

$$\gamma_{xy} \equiv \frac{\pi}{2} - \phi \quad \text{(in radians)}$$

Then

$$\varepsilon_{xy} = \tfrac{1}{2}\gamma_{xy}$$

It is important to define the shear strain ε_{xy} to be one-half the angle γ_{xy} in order to use tensor notation. However, in many texts and papers the shear strain is defined as γ_{xy}. One must take care to notice which definition

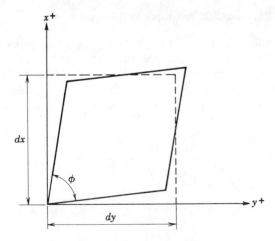

Fig. 1.2. Shearing of a control element.

is used in a text or a research paper, in order to obtain correct results in subsequent analysis.

An isotropic material is one in which the mechanical and physical properties do not vary with orientation. In mathematically modeling an isotropic material, the constant of proportionality between a normal stress and the resulting extensional strain (in the sense of the one-dimensional tensile tests studied in mechanics of materials) is called the modulus of elasticity, E.

Similarly, in the mechanics of materials, the constant of proportionality between a shear stress and the resulting angle γ_{ij} described earlier, in a state of pure shear, is called the shear modulus, G.

One final quantity must be defined—Poisson's ratio, denoted by ν. It is the ratio of the negative of the strain in the j direction to the strain in the $\imath$ direction caused by a stress in the i direction, σ_{ii}. With this definition it is a positive quantity of magnitude $0 \leqslant \nu \leqslant 0.5$ for all known isotropic materials.

The well-known relationship between the modulus of elasticity, the shear modulus, and Poisson's ratio should be remembered:

$$G = \frac{E}{2(1+\nu)}$$

The basic equations of elasticity for a control element of an elastic body in a Cartesian reference frame can now be written. They are written in full, but the compact Einsteinian notation of tensor calculus is also provided in parentheses.

1.1.1. Equilibrium Equations ($\sigma_{ki,k} + F_i = 0$)

A material point within an elastic body can be acted on by two types of forces: body forces (F_i) and surface tractions. The former are forces that are proportional to the mass, such as magnetic forces. The latter are stresses caused by neighboring control elements. In the case of no body forces, the force equilibrium in the x, y, and z directions, respectively, is as follows:

$$\frac{\partial \sigma_x}{\partial x} + \frac{\partial \sigma_{yx}}{\partial y} + \frac{\partial \sigma_{zx}}{\partial z} = 0 \tag{1.1}$$

$$\frac{\partial \sigma_{xy}}{\partial x} + \frac{\partial \sigma_y}{\partial y} + \frac{\partial \sigma_{zy}}{\partial z} = 0 \tag{1.2}$$

$$\frac{\partial \sigma_{xz}}{\partial x} + \frac{\partial \sigma_{yz}}{\partial y} + \frac{\partial \sigma_z}{\partial z} = 0 \tag{1.3}$$

1.1.2. Stress-Strain Relations $(\sigma_{ij} = C_{ijkl}\varepsilon_{kl})$

The relationships between the stresses and strains at a material point in a three-dimensional body mathematically describe the way the material behaves. They are often referred to as the constitutive equations.

$$\varepsilon_x = \frac{1}{E}\left[\sigma_x - \nu(\sigma_y + \sigma_z)\right] \tag{1.4}$$

$$\varepsilon_y = \frac{1}{E}\left[\sigma_y - \nu(\sigma_x + \sigma_z)\right] \tag{1.5}$$

$$\varepsilon_z = \frac{1}{E}\left[\sigma_z - \nu(\sigma_x + \sigma_y)\right] \tag{1.6}$$

$$\varepsilon_{xy} = \frac{1}{2G}\sigma_{xy} \quad \text{where} \quad G = \frac{E}{2(1+\nu)} \tag{1.7}$$

$$\varepsilon_{yz} = \frac{1}{2G}\sigma_{yz} \tag{1.8}$$

$$\varepsilon_{zx} = \frac{1}{2G}\sigma_{zx} \tag{1.9}$$

1.1.3. Linear Strain-Displacement Relations $[\varepsilon_{ij} = \frac{1}{2}(u_{i,j} + u_{j,i})]$

The strain-displacement relations are the kinematic equations relating the displacements that result from an elastic body being strained because of applied loads, or the strains that occur in the material when an elastic body is displaced.

$$\varepsilon_x = \frac{\partial u}{\partial x} \tag{1.10}$$

$$\varepsilon_y = \frac{\partial v}{\partial y} \tag{1.11}$$

$$\varepsilon_z = \frac{\partial w}{\partial z} \tag{1.12}$$

$$\varepsilon_{xy} = \frac{1}{2}\left(\frac{\partial u}{\partial y} + \frac{\partial v}{\partial x}\right) \tag{1.13}$$

$$\varepsilon_{xz} = \frac{1}{2}\left(\frac{\partial u}{\partial z} + \frac{\partial w}{\partial x}\right) \tag{1.14}$$

$$\varepsilon_{yz} = \frac{1}{2}\left(\frac{\partial v}{\partial z} + \frac{\partial w}{\partial y}\right) \tag{1.15}$$

1.1.4. Compatibility Equations $(\varepsilon_{ij,kl} + \varepsilon_{kl,ij} - \varepsilon_{ik,jl} - \varepsilon_{jl,ik} = 0)$

The purpose of the compatibility equations is to ensure that the displacements of an elastic body are single-valued and continuous.

$$\frac{\partial^2 \varepsilon_{xx}}{\partial y \partial z} = \frac{\partial}{\partial x}\left(-\frac{\partial \varepsilon_{yz}}{\partial x} + \frac{\partial \varepsilon_{zx}}{\partial y} + \frac{\partial \varepsilon_{xy}}{\partial z}\right) \tag{1.16}$$

$$\frac{\partial^2 \varepsilon_{yy}}{\partial z \partial x} = \frac{\partial}{\partial y}\left(-\frac{\partial \varepsilon_{zx}}{\partial y} + \frac{\partial \varepsilon_{xy}}{\partial z} + \frac{\partial \varepsilon_{yz}}{\partial x}\right) \tag{1.17}$$

$$\frac{\partial^2 \varepsilon_{zz}}{\partial x \partial y} = \frac{\partial}{\partial \zeta}\left(-\frac{\partial \varepsilon_{xy}}{\partial z} + \frac{\partial \varepsilon_{yz}}{\partial x} + \frac{\partial \varepsilon_{zx}}{\partial y}\right) \tag{1.18}$$

$$2\frac{\partial^2 \varepsilon_{xy}}{\partial x \partial y} = \frac{\partial^2 \varepsilon_{xx}}{\partial y^2} + \frac{\partial^2 \varepsilon_{yy}}{\partial x^2} \tag{1.19}$$

$$2\frac{\partial^2 \varepsilon_{yz}}{\partial y \partial z} = \frac{\partial^2 \varepsilon_{yy}}{\partial z^2} + \frac{\partial^2 \varepsilon_{zz}}{\partial y^2} \tag{1.20}$$

$$2\frac{\partial^2 \varepsilon_{zx}}{\partial z \partial x} = \frac{\partial^2 \varepsilon_{zz}}{\partial x^2} + \frac{\partial^2 \varepsilon_{xx}}{\partial z^2} \tag{1.21}$$

Because of the symmetry of the stress and strain tensors,

$$\sigma_{ij} = \sigma_{ji} \quad \text{and} \quad \varepsilon_{ij} = \varepsilon_{ji} \quad (i,j = x,y,z)$$

the unknowns in the above equations are: six stress components, six strain components, and three displacements.

When a form for the displacements or strains is assumed such that the displacements are guaranteed to be continuous and single-valued everywhere in the region under consideration, the compatibility equations are automatically satisfied and need not be used. Under that condition there are 15 equations, namely Equations (1.1) through (1.15), and mathematically the problem of solving them is well posed.

1.2. ASSUMPTIONS OF PLATE THEORY

In classical, linear thin-plate theory, there are a number of assumptions that are necessary in order to reduce the three-dimensional equations of elasticity to a two-dimensional set that can be solved. Consider an elastic body as shown in Figure 1.3, comprising the region $0 \leqslant x \leqslant a$, $0 \leqslant y \leqslant b$, and $-h/2 \leqslant h/2$, such that $h \ll a$ and $h \ll b$. This is called a plate.

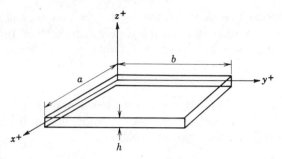

Fig. 1.3. Rectangular plate.

The following assumptions are made.

1. A lineal element of the plate extending through the plate thickness, normal to the midsurface x-y plane, in the unstressed state, on the application of load: (a) undergoes at most a translation and a rotation with respect to the original coordinate system, and (b) remains normal to the deformed middle surface.

2. A plate resists lateral and in-plane loads by bending, transverse shear stresses, and in-plane action, not through blocklike compression or tension in the plate in the thickness direction. This assumption results from the fact that $h/a \ll 1$ and $h/b \ll 1$.

From 1(a) the following is implied:

3. A lineal element through the thickness does not elongate or contract.
4. The lineal element remains straight upon load application.

In addition,

5. St. Venant's principle applies.

It is seen from 1(a) that the most general form for the two in-plane displacements is:

$$u(x,y,z) = u_0(x,y) + z\alpha(x,y)$$

$$v(x,y,z) = v_0(x,y) + z\beta(x,y)$$

where u_0 and v_0 are the in-plane middle surface displacements ($z = 0$), and α and β are rotations undefined as yet. Assumption 3 requires that $\varepsilon_z = 0$, which in turn means that the lateral deflection w is a function of x and y only [from Equation (1.12)]:

$$w = w(x,y)$$

Also, Equation (1.6) is ignored.

Assumption 4 requires that for any z, ε_{xz} = constant and ε_{yz} = constant at any specific location (x,y) on the plate middle surface, for all z. Assumption 1(b) requires that the constant should be zero; hence

$$\varepsilon_{xz} = \varepsilon_{yz} = 0$$

Assumption 2 means that $\sigma_z = 0$ in the stress-strain relations.

Incidentally, the assumptions above are identical to those of the classical theory of thin beams, rings, and shells.

1.3. DERIVATION OF THE EQUILIBRIUM EQUATIONS FOR A PLATE

Figure 1.4 shows the positive directions of stress quantities to be defined when the plate is subjected to lateral and in-plane loads. The stress couples are defined as follows:

$$M_x = \int_{-h/2}^{h/2} \sigma_x z \, dz \tag{1.22}$$

$$M_y = \int_{-h/2}^{+h/2} \sigma_y z \, dz \tag{1.23}$$

$$M_{xy} = \int_{-h/2}^{h/2} \sigma_{xy} z \, dz \tag{1.24}$$

$$M_{yx} = \int_{-h/2}^{h/2} \sigma_{yx} z \, dz = M_{xy} \tag{1.25}$$

Physically, it is seen that the stress couple is the summation of the moments about the middle surface of all the stresses acting on all the infinitesimal control elements through the plate thickness at a location (x,y). In the limit the summation is replaced by integration.

Similarly, the transverse shear resultants are defined as

$$Q_x = \int_{-h/2}^{h/2} \sigma_{xz} \, dz \tag{1.26}$$

$$Q_y = \int_{-h/2}^{h/2} \sigma_{yz} \, dz \tag{1.27}$$

Again, the shear resultant, physically, is the summation of all the shear stresses in the thickness direction acting on all the infinitesimal control

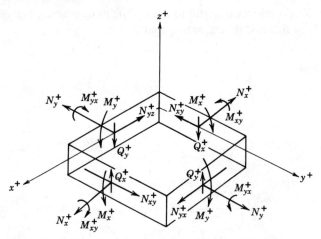

Fig. 1.4. Positive directions of stress resultants and couples.

elements across the plate thickness at a plate location (x,y).
Finally, the in-plane stress resultants are defined to be

$$N_x = \int_{-h/2}^{h/2} \sigma_x \, dz \tag{1.28}$$

$$N_y = \int_{-h/2}^{h/2} \sigma_y \, dz \tag{1.29}$$

$$N_{xy} = \int_{-h/2}^{h/2} \sigma_{xy} \, dz \tag{1.30}$$

$$N_{yx} = \int_{-h/2}^{h/2} \sigma_{yx} \, dz = N_{xy} \tag{1.31}$$

These then are the sums of all the in-plane stresses acting on all of the infinitesimal control elements across the thickness of the plate at (x,y).

Thus, in plate theory, the details of each control element under consideration are disregarded when one integrates the stress quantities across the thickness h. Instead of considering stresses at each material point, one really deals with the integrated stress quantities defined above. The procedure for obtaining the governing equations for plates from the equations of elasticity is to perform certain integrations on them.

Proceeding, multiply Equation (1.1) by $z\,dz$ and integrate between $-h/2$ to $+h/2$, as follows, remembering that $\sigma_{ij} = \sigma_{ji}$:

$$\int_{-h/2}^{h/2} \left(z \frac{\partial \sigma_x}{\partial x} + z \frac{\partial \sigma_{xy}}{\partial y} + z \frac{\partial \sigma_{xz}}{\partial z} \right) dz = 0$$

$$\frac{\partial}{\partial x} \int_{-h/2}^{h/2} \sigma_x z\,dz + \frac{\partial}{\partial y} \int_{-h/2}^{h/2} \sigma_{xy} z\,dz + \int_{-h/2}^{h/2} z \frac{\partial \sigma_{xz}}{\partial z}\,dz = 0$$

$$\frac{\partial M_x}{\partial x} + \frac{\partial M_{xy}}{\partial y} + z\sigma_{xz} \big]_{-h/2}^{h/2} - \int_{-h/2}^{h/2} \sigma_{xz}\,dz = 0$$

In the above, the order of differentiation and integration can be reversed because x and z are orthogonal one to the other. Looking at the third term, we see that $\sigma_{xz} = \sigma_{zx} = 0$ when there are no shear loads on the surface. This is not true for laminated plates. There, defining $\tau_{1x} = \sigma_{xz}(+h/2)$ and $\tau_{2x} = \sigma_{xz}(-h/2)$, we obtain the results shown in Equation (1.32). It should also be noted that for plates supported on the edge by knife edges, σ_{xz} does not go to zero at $+h/2$, and so the theory does not give good results at that edge; but by St. Venant's principle, the solutions are satisfactory away from the knife edge.

$$\frac{\partial M_x}{\partial x} + \frac{\partial M_{xy}}{\partial y} + \frac{h}{2}\left(\tau_{1x} + \tau_{2x} \right) - Q_x = 0 \tag{1.32}$$

Likewise Equation (1.2) becomes

$$\frac{\partial M_{xy}}{\partial x} + \frac{\partial M_y}{\partial y} + \frac{h}{2}\left(\tau_{1y} + \tau_{2y} \right) - Q_y = 0 \tag{1.33}$$

where $\quad \tau_{1y} = \sigma_{yz}(+h/2) \quad$ and $\quad \tau_{2y} = \sigma_{yz}(-h/2).$

These two equations describe the moment equilibrium of a plate element. Looking now at Equation (1.3), multiplying it by dz, and integrating between $\pm h/2$, we have

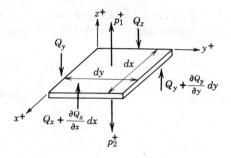

$$\int_{-h/2}^{h/2} \left(\frac{\partial \sigma_{zx}}{\partial x} + \frac{\partial \sigma_{yz}}{\partial y} + \frac{\partial \sigma_z}{\partial z} \right) dz$$

$$= \frac{\partial Q_x}{\partial x} + \frac{\partial Q_y}{\partial y} + \sigma_z \Big]_{-h/2}^{h/2}$$

$$= \frac{\partial Q_x}{\partial x} + \frac{\partial Q_y}{\partial y} + p_1(xy) - p_2(x,y) = 0 \qquad (1.34)$$

where $p_1(x,y) = \sigma_z(+h/2), p_2(x,y) = \sigma_z(-h/2)$.

One could also derive this by considering the vertical equilibrium of a plate element as shown above. One may ask why we make use of σ_z in this equation and not in the stress-strain relation. The difference is not really an inconsistency because σ_z does not appear explicitly in Equation (1.34), and once away from the surface the normal surface traction is absorbed by shear and in-plane stresses rather than by σ_z in the plate interior.

Similarly, multiplying Equations (1.1) and (1.2) by dz, and integrating across the plate thickness results in the plate equilibrium equations in the x and y directions respectively, we have

$$\frac{\partial N_x}{\partial x} + \frac{\partial N_{xy}}{\partial y} + (\tau_{1x} - \tau_{2x}) = 0 \qquad (1.35)$$

$$\frac{\partial N_{xy}}{\partial x} + \frac{\partial N_y}{\partial y} + (\tau_{1y} - \tau_{2y}) = 0 \qquad (1.36)$$

1.4. DERIVATION OF PLATE MOMENT - CURVATURE RELATIONS AND INTEGRATED STRESS RESULTANT DISPLACEMENT RELATIONS

We must now obtain the plate equations corresponding to the stress-strain relations. We do not deal with ε_x, ε_y, and ε_{xy}, since we have averaged the stresses by integrating through the thickness; hence we deal with the displacements. Combining Equations (1.4) through (1.15) gives the following, remembering that σ_z has been assumed zero in the interior of the plate, and excluding Equation (1.6) for reasons given previously:

$$\frac{\partial u}{\partial x} = \frac{1}{E}\left[\sigma_x - \nu\sigma_y\right] \tag{1.37}$$

$$\frac{\partial v}{\partial y} = \frac{1}{E}\left[\sigma_y - \nu\sigma_x\right] \tag{1.38}$$

$$\frac{1}{2}\left(\frac{\partial u}{\partial y} + \frac{\partial v}{\partial x}\right) = \frac{1}{2G}\sigma_{xy} \tag{1.39}$$

$$\frac{1}{2}\left(\frac{\partial v}{\partial z} + \frac{\partial w}{\partial y}\right) = \frac{1}{2G}\sigma_{yz} \tag{1.40}$$

$$\frac{1}{2}\left(\frac{\partial w}{\partial x} + \frac{\partial u}{\partial z}\right) = \frac{1}{2G}\sigma_{xz} \tag{1.41}$$

Next, recall the form of the admissable displacements resulting from the plate-theory assumptions:

$$u = u_0(x,y) + z\alpha(x,y) \tag{1.42}$$

$$v = v_0(x,y) + z\beta(x,y) \tag{1.43}$$

$$w = w(x,y) \quad \text{only} \tag{1.44}$$

In plate theory it is shown that a lineal element through the plate experiences translations and rotations, but no extensions or contractions. For these assumptions to be valid, the lateral deflections must be small compared to the plate thickness. It should be noted that if a plate is very thin, lateral loads can cause lateral deflections many times the thickness, and the plate then behaves largely as a membrane, because it has little or no bending resistance.

The assumptions of classical plate theory require that transverse shear deformation be zero. If $\varepsilon_{xz} = \varepsilon_{yz} = 0$, then from Equations (1.14) and (1.15),

$$\frac{1}{2}\left(\frac{\partial u}{\partial z} + \frac{\partial w}{\partial x}\right) = 0 \quad \text{or} \quad \frac{\partial u}{\partial z} = -\frac{\partial w}{\partial x}$$

Likewise

$$\frac{\partial v}{\partial z} = -\frac{\partial w}{\partial y}$$

Hence, from Equations (1.42) and (1.43), it is seen that the rotations are

$$\alpha = -\frac{\partial w}{\partial x} \tag{1.45}$$

$$\beta = -\frac{\partial w}{\partial y} \tag{1.46}$$

Using Equations (1.42) and (1.37), multiplying Equation (1.37) through by $z\,dz$, and integrating from $-h/2$ to $+h/2$, one obtains

$$\int_{-h/2}^{h/2} \frac{\partial u_o}{\partial x} z\,dz + \int_{-h/2}^{h/2} z^2 \frac{\partial \alpha}{\partial x}\,dz = \int_{-h/2}^{h/2} \frac{1}{E}[\sigma_x - \nu\sigma_y]z\,dz \tag{1.47}$$

Likewise Equations (1.43) and (1.38) result in

$$\int_{-h/2}^{h/2} \frac{\partial v_o}{\partial y} z\,dz + \int_{-h/2}^{h/2} z^2 \frac{\partial \beta}{\partial y}\,dz = \int_{-h/2}^{h/2} \frac{1}{E}[\sigma_y - \nu\sigma_x]z\,dz \tag{1.48}$$

and Equations (1.42), (1.43), and (1.39) give

$$\int_{-h/2}^{h/2} \left(\frac{\partial u_o}{\partial y} + \frac{\partial v_o}{\partial x}\right) z\,dz + \int_{-h/2}^{h/2} \left(z^2 \frac{\partial \alpha}{\partial y} + z^2 \frac{\partial \beta}{\partial x}\right) dz = \int_{-h/2}^{h/2} \frac{1}{G}\sigma_{xy}z\,dz \tag{1.49}$$

Integrating Equations (1.47), (1.48), and (1.49) gives, using Equations (1.45) and (1.46),

$$\frac{h^3}{12}\frac{\partial \alpha}{\partial x} = \frac{1}{E}[M_x - \nu M_y] = -\frac{h^3}{12}\frac{\partial^2 w}{\partial x^2} \tag{1.50}$$

$$\frac{h^3}{12}\frac{\partial \beta}{\partial y} = \frac{1}{E}[M_y - \nu M_x] = -\frac{h^3}{12}\frac{\partial^2 w}{\partial y^2} \tag{1.51}$$

$$\frac{h^3}{12}\left(\frac{\partial \alpha}{\partial y} + \frac{\partial \beta}{\partial x}\right) = \frac{1}{G}M_{xy} = -\frac{h^3}{6}\frac{\partial^2 w}{\partial x \partial y} \tag{1.52}$$

Since $G = E/2(1 + \nu)$,

$$M_{xy} = -(1 - \nu)D\frac{\partial^2 w}{\partial x \partial y} \quad \text{where} \quad D = \frac{Eh^3}{12(1 - \nu^2)} \quad (1.54)$$

Solving Equations (1.50) and (1.51) for M_x and M_y results in

$$M_x = -D\left[\frac{\partial^2 w}{\partial x^2} + \nu\frac{\partial^2 w}{\partial y^2} \right] \quad (1.55)$$

$$M_y = -D\left[\frac{\partial^2 w}{\partial y^2} + \nu\frac{\partial^2 w}{\partial x^2} \right] \quad (1.56)$$

Equations (1.54) through (1.56) are known as the moment-curvature relations, and D is seen to be the flexural stiffness of the plate.

Likewise, substituting Equations (1.54) through (1.56) into Equations (1.32) and (1.33) results in

$$Q_x = -D\frac{\partial}{\partial x}(\nabla^2 w) + \frac{h}{2}(\tau_{1x} + \tau_{2x}) \quad (1.57)$$

$$Q_y = -D\frac{\partial}{\partial y}(\nabla^2 w) + \frac{h}{2}(\tau_{1y} + \tau_{2y}), \quad (1.58)$$

where $(\nabla^2 w) = \dfrac{\partial^2 w}{\partial x^2} + \dfrac{\partial^2 w}{\partial y^2}$.

Also, using Equations (1.42) and (1.43), substituting them into Equations (1.37) through (1.39), then multiplying the latter three equations by dz, and integrating across the thickness results in the following integrated stress-strain relationships:

$$N_x = K\left[\frac{\partial u_0}{\partial x} + \nu\frac{\partial v_0}{\partial y} \right] \quad (1.59)$$

$$N_y = K\left[\frac{\partial v_0}{\partial y} + \nu\frac{\partial u_0}{\partial x} \right] \quad (1.60)$$

$$N_{xy} = N_{yx} = Gh\left[\frac{\partial u_0}{\partial y} + \frac{\partial v_0}{\partial x} \right] \quad (1.61)$$

where $Eh/(1 - \nu^2) = K$.

Equations (1.59) through (1.61) describe the in-plane force and deformation behavior, and K is the extensional stiffness.

1.5. DERIVATION OF THE GOVERNING EQUATIONS FOR A PLATE

The equations governing the lateral deflections, bending, and shearing action of a plate are

$$\frac{\partial M_x}{\partial x} + \frac{\partial M_{xy}}{\partial y} - Q_x + \frac{h}{2}(\tau_{1x} + \tau_{2x}) = 0 \tag{1.62}$$

$$\frac{\partial M_{xy}}{\partial x} + \frac{\partial M_y}{\partial y} - Q_y + \frac{h}{2}(\tau_{1y} + \tau_{2y}) = 0 \tag{1.63}$$

$$\frac{\partial Q_x}{\partial x} + \frac{\partial Q_y}{\partial y} + p_1 - p_2 = 0 \tag{1.64}$$

$$M_x = -D\left[\frac{\partial^2 w}{\partial w^2} + \nu\frac{\partial^2 w}{\partial y^2}\right] \tag{1.65}$$

$$M_y = -D\left[\frac{\partial^2 w}{\partial y^2} + \nu\frac{\partial^2 w}{\partial x^2}\right] \tag{1.66}$$

$$M_{xy} = -(1-\nu)D\frac{\partial^2 w}{\partial x\partial y} \tag{1.67}$$

The equations governing the in-plane stress resultants and in-plane midsurface displacements are:

$$\frac{\partial N_x}{\partial x} + \frac{\partial N_{xy}}{\partial y} + (\tau_{1x} - \tau_{2x}) = 0 \tag{1.68}$$

$$\frac{\partial N_{xy}}{\partial x} + \frac{\partial N_y}{\partial y} + (\tau_{1y} - \tau_{2y}) = 0 \tag{1.69}$$

$$N_x = K\left[\frac{\partial u_0}{\partial x} + \nu\frac{\partial v_0}{\partial y}\right] \tag{1.70}$$

$$N_y = K\left[\frac{\partial v_0}{\partial y} + \nu\frac{\partial u_0}{\partial x}\right] \tag{1.71}$$

$$N_{yx} = Gh\left[\frac{\partial u_0}{\partial y} + \frac{\partial v_0}{\partial x}\right] \tag{1.72}$$

It should be noted that in classical thin-plate theory the equations related to bending and shear, Equations (1.62) through (1.67), are completely uncoupled from the equations related to in-plane loads and displacements, Equations (1.68) through (1.72). [*Note*: In Chapter 5, we see that when in-plane loads are highly compressive, they do indeed cause lateral displacements (buckling), but a more sophisticated theory is evolved for that case.]

It should also be noted that the flexural stiffness D of the plate corresponds closely to EI in beam theory, but is in terms of a unit width, and incorporates the Poisson-ratio effect. A similar correspondence exists between the extensional stiffness K and EA in beam theory.

Equations (1.62) through (1.72) are the 11 governing plate equations. First note that the plate can tell only the difference between normal tractions on the upper and lower surfaces. Hence we define

$$p_1(x,y) - p_2(x,y) \equiv p(x,y) \tag{1.73}$$

Substituting Equations (1.62) and (1.63) in Equation (1.64) results in the following for the case of no shear stresses on the upper and lower surfaces of the plate:

$$\frac{\partial^2 M_x}{\partial x^2} + 2\frac{\partial^2 M_{xy}}{\partial x \partial y} + \frac{\partial^2 M_y}{\partial y^2} + p(x,y) = 0$$

Substituting Equations (1.65), (1.66), and (1.67) in this results in

$$-D\left[\frac{\partial^4 w}{\partial x^4} + \nu\frac{\partial^4 w}{\partial x^2 \partial y^2}\right] - 2(1-\nu)D\frac{\partial^4 w}{\partial x^2 \partial y^2} - D\left[\frac{\partial^4 w}{\partial y^4} + \nu\frac{\partial^4 w}{\partial x^2 \partial y^2}\right] + p(x,y) = 0$$

$$D\left[\frac{\partial^4 w}{\partial x^4} + 2\frac{\partial^4 w}{\partial x^2 \partial y^2} + \frac{\partial^4 w}{\partial y^4}\right] = p(x,y)$$

$$D\nabla^4 w = p(x,y) \tag{1.74}$$

where

$$\nabla^2(\ ) = \frac{\partial^2(\ )}{\partial x^2} + \frac{\partial^2(\ )}{\partial y^2} \quad \text{and} \quad \nabla^4(\ ) = \nabla^2(\nabla^2(\ ))$$

∇^2 is the sum of the curvatures in two orthogonal directions at the location

(x,y) in the plate. ∇^4 is thus the sum of the curvatures of the sum of the curvatures in orthogonal directions. One might say that it is a measure of "bulginess."

Next, treating Equations (1.68) through (1.72), by substituting Equations (1.70) through (1.72) into the two equilibrium equations, we obtain after considerable manipulation, and for the case of no surface shear stresses,

$$\nabla^4 u_0 = 0 \tag{1.75}$$

$$\nabla^4 v_0 = 0 \tag{1.76}$$

Equation (1.74) can now be used to discuss some other similar equations. By merely setting $\partial()/\partial y = 0$, letting $\nu = 0$, and multiplying by b, Equation (1.74) becomes the governing differential equation for a beam,

$$EI\frac{d^4 w}{dx^4} = q(x) = bp(x) \tag{1.77}$$

where b is the width of the beam, $I = bh^3/12$ for a beam of rectangular cross section, and $q(x)$ is the load per unit length of the beam.

For a vibrating plate, an inertial load per unit planform area is added as an equivalent force per unit area, resulting in

$$D\nabla^4 w = p(x,y,t) - \rho h\frac{\partial^2 w}{\partial t^2} \tag{1.78}$$

where ρ is the mass density of the plate material, and t is the time. Here $w = w(x,y,t)$.

In a plate of varying thickness, $h = h(x,y)$, the following equation is derived rather than Equation (1.74):

$$\nabla^2(D\nabla^2 w) - (1 - \nu)\Diamond^4(D,w) = p(x,y) \tag{1.79}$$

where $\Diamond^4$ is the die operator defined as

$$\Diamond^4(D,w) = \frac{\partial^2 D}{\partial x^2}\frac{\partial^2 w}{\partial y^2} - 2\frac{\partial^2 D}{\partial x \partial y}\frac{\partial^2 w}{\partial x \partial y} + \frac{\partial^2 D}{\partial y^2}\frac{\partial^2 w}{\partial x^2} \tag{1.80}$$

If a plate is on an elastic foundation in which a linear foundation modulus k in units of lb/(in.)(in.^{2}) can be defined, then Equation (1.74) is altered by adding in the additional lateral force per unit planform area:

$$D\nabla^4 w = p(x,y) - kw \tag{1.81}$$

1.6. BOUNDARY CONDITIONS

First we discuss the boundary conditions for the bending of a plate subjected to lateral loads, Equation (1.74). Additional boundary conditions for Equations (1.75) and (1.76) for a plate subjected also to in-plane loads or displacements are discussed at the end of this section.

Since we have a fourth-order partial differential equation in x and y describing the bending of a plate given by Equation (1.74), four boundary conditions are needed on the x edges and four are needed on the y edges, that is, two on each edge. For the clamped and simply supported edges, knowledge of beam theory dictates the following:

For a clamped edge	For a simply supported edge	
$w = 0$	$w = 0$	
$\dfrac{\partial w}{\partial n} = 0$	$M_n = 0$	(1.82)

where n is the directional normal to the edge.

1.6.1. Free Edge

Consider an $x = $ constant free edge. Since by definition a free edge has no loads applied to it, Figure 1.3 shows that M_x, M_{xy}, and Q_x all are zero there. Hence six boundary conditions must be satisfied on the two x = constant plate edges. However, the plate equation is only fourth order in x; hence we cannot specify more than two boundary conditions on each edge. [*Note*: In a more advanced plate theory that includes the effects of transverse shear deformation ($\varepsilon_{xz} \neq 0$ and $\varepsilon_{yz} \neq 0$), the governing equations are sixth order in both x and y, and this problem does not occur.]

To eliminate the problem, Kirchoff proceeded as follows: On the free $x = $ constant edge, M_x is set equal to zero. The twisting stress couple M_{xy} is considered to consist of two forces of magnitude M_{xy} separated by a small distance dy, as shown in Sketch 1.1 below. Since the stress couple M_{xy} is not constant in general along an edge, nearby is another couple, $M_{xy} + (\partial M_{xy}/\partial y)dy$. It too can be regarded as two forces of magnitude $M_{xy} + (\partial M_{xy}/\partial y)dy$, separated by a distance dy. Therefore, considering an infinitesimal region of the edge shown within the dotted line, it is seen that

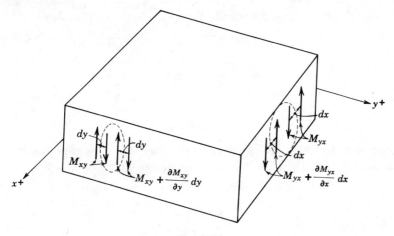

Sketch 1.1

there is a force M_{xy} positive downward and a force $M_{xy}+(\partial M_{xy}/\partial y)dy$ positive upward as well as the force due to the transverse shear resultant $Q_x\,dy$ acting positive upward. These must equal zero; hence

$$-M_{xy}+M_{xy}+\frac{\partial M_{xy}}{\partial y}\,dy+Q_x\,dy=0$$

or

$$V_x\equiv Q_x+\frac{\partial M_{xy}}{\partial y}=0 \tag{1.83}$$

where V_x is called the effective shear resultant on a free edge.

Although physically both Q_x and M_{xy} are each equal to zero on an $x=$ constant free edge, the approximation given in Equation (1.83) is found to have sufficient accuracy for plates of classical proportions, and is widely used in plate analysis. It is known as the Kirchoff boundary condition.

Likewise on a $y=$ constant free edge,

$$V_y\equiv Q_y+\frac{\partial M_{yx}}{\partial x}=0 \tag{1.84}$$

and of course on any edge the other boundary condition is

$$M_n=0 \tag{1.85}$$

where n refers to the direction normal to the edge.

1.6.2. Edge Elastically Supported against Deflection

Sketch 1.2

Suppose the linear spring constant of a support at an edge is c lb/in.^{2} (see Sketch 1.2). Then the boundary conditions become

$$M_n = 0 \tag{1.85}$$

$$V_n + cw = 0 \tag{1.86}$$

$$Q_n + \frac{\partial M_{ns}}{\partial s} + cw = 0 \quad \text{or}$$

$$\frac{\partial^3 w}{\partial n^3} + (2 - \nu)\frac{\partial^3 w}{\partial n \partial s^2} - \frac{cw}{D} = 0 \tag{1.87}$$

where s refers to the direction parallel to the edge.

1.6.3. In-Plane Boundary Conditions

In Section 1.5 it was seen that the governing equations involving the in-plane forces and midsurface displacements are completely uncoupled from the other equations, the boundary conditions for which have been discussed above.

In the case where a plate is not subjected to any prescribed in-plane loads or prescribed midsurface displacements, the solutions to Equations (1.75) and (1.76) are

$$u_0 = v_0 = 0$$

For other cases, the details of the edge conditions of the plate structure being analyzed must be studied in detail, to specify what boundary conditions should be prescribed. However, through the use of variational procedures, which are discussed in Chapter 6, it can be shown that the boundary conditions to use in solving Equations (1.75) and (1.76) are

> For an $x = $ constant edge:
> Either u_0 is prescribed or $N_x = 0$
> and
> either v_0 is prescribed or $N_{xy} = 0$.

For an $y = $ constant edge:
Either v_0 is prescribed or $N_y = 0$
and
either u_0 is prescribed or $N_{yx} = 0$.

1.7. STRESS DISTRIBUTION WITHIN A PLATE

In the plate theory, because all equations are integrated across the thickness, only integrated stress quantities are known. For stresses at a control element or material point within a plate, one must *assume* a stress distribution. This is done by means of an analogy with beam theory. Thus

$$\sigma_x = \frac{M_x z}{h^3/12} + \frac{N_x}{h} \tag{1.88}$$

$$\sigma_y = \frac{M_y z}{h^3/12} + \frac{N_y}{h} \tag{1.89}$$

$$\sigma_{xy} = \frac{M_{xy} z}{h^3/12} + \frac{N_{xy}}{h} \tag{1.90}$$

$$\sigma_{xz} = \frac{3Q_x}{2h}\left[1 - \left(\frac{z}{h/2}\right)^2\right] - \frac{S_x}{4} \tag{1.91}$$

$$\sigma_{yz} = \frac{3Q_y}{2h}\left[1 - \left(\frac{z}{h/2}\right)^2\right] - \frac{S_y}{4} \tag{1.92}$$

where

$$S_x = \tau_{1x}\left[1 - 2\left(\frac{z}{h/2}\right) - 3\left(\frac{z}{h/2}\right)^2\right]$$

$$+ \tau_{2x}\left[1 + 2\left(\frac{z}{h/2}\right) - 3\left(\frac{z}{h/2}\right)^2\right]$$

$$S_y = \tau_{1y}\left[1 - 2\left(\frac{z}{h/2}\right) - 3\left(\frac{z}{h/2}\right)^2\right]$$

$$+ \tau_{2y}\left[1 + 2\left(\frac{z}{h/2}\right) - 3\left(\frac{z}{h/2}\right)^2\right]$$

It can be shown easily that these distributions satisfy the definitions of Equations (1.22) through (1.31). Equally important, they satisfy the equilibrium equations of elasticity [(1.1) and (1.2)] exactly, and Equation (1.3) on the average. Thus the stresses obtained through the use of plate theory (or beam, shell, and ring theory) are not exact, in the sense of being three-dimensional elasticity-theory solutions, but they are very close to the exact solution.

1.8. REFERENCES

1. I. S. Sokolnikoff, *Mathematical Theory of Elasticity*, 2nd ed., McGraw-Hill, 1956.
2. S. Timoshenko and A. Woinowsky-Krieger, *Theory of Plates and Shells*, 2nd ed., McGraw-Hill, 1959.
3. K. Marguerre and H. T. Woernle, *Elastic Plates*, Blaisdell, 1970.

1.9. PROBLEMS

1.1. The governing equations for a plate under lateral load $p(x,y)$ are given by Equations (1.74) through (1.76). However, when the plate is subjected to surface shear stress, additional terms are added which are functions, call them f, g, and h, of τ_{1x}, τ_{2x}, τ_{1y}, and τ_{2y}, such that

$$D\nabla^4 w = p(x,y) + f(\tau_{1x},\tau_{2x},\tau_{1y},\tau_{2y})$$

$$K\nabla^4 u_0 = g(\tau_{1x},\tau_{2x},\tau_{1y},\tau_{2y})$$

$$K\nabla^4 v_0 = h(\tau_{1x},\tau_{2x},\tau_{1y},\tau_{2y})$$

Find f, g, and h.

1.2. Derive Equation (1.79), starting from Equation (1.62) through (1.67).

1.3. Show that the stress distributions of Section 1.7 do in fact satisfy the definition of Equation (1.22) through (1.31).

1.4. Show that the stress distributions of Section 1.7 satisfy Equations (1.1) and (1.2).

1.5. Starting with the pertinent elasticity equations, derive Equations (1.68) and (1.70).

2

SOLUTIONS TO PROBLEMS
OF RECTANGULAR PLATES

2.1. PURE BENDING OF A PLATE

Here M_x, M_y are given and constant, and $M_{xy} = 0$, as shown in Sketch 2.1. Then from Equation (1.65), (1.66), and (1.67).

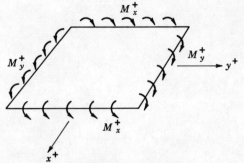

Sketch 2.1

$$-\frac{M_x}{D} = \frac{\partial^2 w}{\partial x^2} + v\frac{\partial^2 w}{\partial y^2} \tag{2.1}$$

$$-\frac{M_y}{D} = \frac{\partial^2 w}{\partial y^2} + v\frac{\partial^2 w}{\partial x^2} \tag{2.2}$$

$$0 = \frac{\partial^2 w}{\partial x \partial y} \tag{2.3}$$

Assume the lateral deflection to be of the form

$$w(x,y) = f(x) + g(y) \tag{2.4}$$

Substitution of Equation (2.4) into Equations (2.1) and (2.2) gives

$$f''(x) + vg''(y) = -\frac{M_x}{D}$$

$$g''(y) + vf''(x) = -\frac{M_y}{D}$$

Manipulation of these equations results in

$$f''(x) = -\frac{M_x - vM_y}{D(1-v^2)}$$

Integrating this twice provides

$$f(x) = -\frac{M_x - vM_y}{2D(1-v^2)}x^2 + C_1 x + C_2 \tag{2.5}$$

Likewise $g(y)$ is found to be

$$g(y) = -\frac{M_y - \nu M_x}{2D(1-\nu^2)}y^2 + C_3 y + C_4 \qquad (2.6)$$

Thus the most general form for the deflection is

$$w(x,y) = -\frac{M_x - \nu M_y}{2D(1-\nu^2)}x^2 - \frac{M_y - \nu M_x}{2D(1-\nu^2)}y^2 + C_1 x + C_3 y + C_5 \qquad (2.7)$$

We now choose the origin of the axes such that

$$w(0,0) = 0$$

$$\frac{\partial w}{\partial x}(0,0) = 0$$

$$\frac{\partial w}{\partial y}(0,0) = 0$$

Then $C_1 = C_3 = C_5 = 0$.

Incidentally, the solutions discussed in this section are not only plate-theory solutions but solutions of the three-dimensional elasticity equations as well. Hence, plate theory is exact for cases of plates under pure bending.

Case I. Pure Bending: Synclastic Case

Let $M_x = M_y = M$. Equation (2.7) then becomes

$$w(x,y) = -\frac{M}{2D(1+\nu)}(x^2 + y^2) \qquad (2.8)$$

It is seen that at a given radius r, where $x^2 + y^2 \equiv r^2$, the lateral deflection w for all points on that circle of radius r is identical. The curved surface of the plate is a paraboloid of revolution. Also, it is seen that

$$\frac{\partial^2 w}{\partial x^2} = \frac{\partial^2 w}{\partial y^2} = -\frac{M}{D(1+\nu)} \qquad (2.9)$$

Thus the curvatures in the x and y directions are equal. In fact it can be shown that the curvature in any direction is the same, and the stress couple in any direction and at any location is M, a constant. This result is not limited as to the size or shape of the plate. So in general a plate of any shape, if its edges are subjected to a constant stress couple M, deforms to a paraboloid of revolution, has a constant curvature, and has a constant stress field.

If $M_x \neq M_y$, the loci of points with the same lateral deflection form an ellipse. When $M_x M_y > 0$, the deformed surface of the plate is termed synclastic; when $M_x M_y < 0$, it is termed anticlastic or saddle-shaped.

Case II. Pure Bending: Anticlastic Case

Let $M_x = -M = -M_y$. From Equation (2.7), and referred to the same origin as before so that C_1, C_3, and C_5 are all zero, the lateral deflection is given by

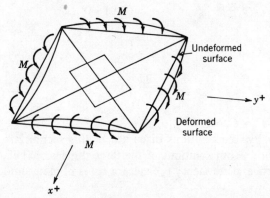

Sketch 2.2

$$w(x,y) = \frac{+M}{2D(1-\nu)}(x^2 - y^2) \qquad (2.10)$$

It is seen that when $x^2 - y^2 = 0$, $w = 0$, that is, diagonals through the origin $(y = \pm x)$ do not deflect at all. For lines parallel to diagonals, given by $y = x + a$, so that

$$y^2 = x^2 + 2ax + a^2$$

we see from Equation (2.10) that the lateral deflection is

$$w(x,y) = \frac{M}{2D(1-\nu)}(-2ax - a^2)$$

This line therefore remains straight and has experienced only a rigid-body rotation. If a set of four lines parallel to the diagonals are chosen as shown in Sketch 2.2, so that their perpendicular distances to the origin are equal, then the enclosed area is subjected to pure twist only, and there is no bending moment acting on this portion of the plate.

2.2. SOME GENERAL SOLUTIONS OF THE BIHARMONIC EQUATIONS

The governing equation for a rectangular plate subjected to lateral loads is given by

$$\nabla^4 w = \frac{\partial^4 w}{\partial x^4} + 2\frac{\partial^4 w}{\partial x^2 \partial y^2} + \frac{\partial^4 w}{\partial y^4} = \frac{p(x,y)}{D} \tag{2.11}$$

We first solve the homogeneous equation, $\nabla^4 w = 0$. It is interesting to do this to identify the functions that are solutions to the biharmonic equation.

One of the most common methods used to solve this homogeneous equation is the separation of variables. This can be attempted when the boundary conditions are homogeneous. We cannot count on the separation of variables to yield the complete exact solution, but it does give all the separable solutions. There *may* be others.

Let

$$w(x,y) = X(x)Y(y) \tag{2.12}$$

From Equations (2.11) and (2.12),

$$X^{IV}Y + 2X''Y'' + XY^{IV} = 0$$

Dividing through by XY gives

$$\frac{X^{IV}}{X} + 2\frac{X''}{X}\frac{Y''}{Y} + \frac{Y^{IV}}{Y} = 0 \tag{2.13}$$

The variables are still not separated; hence let

$$\frac{X^{IV}}{X} = f(x), \quad \frac{X''}{X} = g(x), \quad \frac{Y''}{Y} = k(y), \quad \frac{Y^{IV}}{Y} = p(y)$$

Equation (2.13) becomes

$$f(x) + 2g(x)k(y) + p(y) = 0 \tag{2.14}$$

Differentiating with respect to x gives

$$f'(x) + 2g'(x)k(y) = 0$$

or

$$\frac{f'(x)}{g'(x)} + 2k(y) = 0$$

For this to be true, we must have $f'(x)/g'(x) = $ constant and $k(y)$ = constant. Thus

$$k(y) = -\lambda^2 = \text{constant} \qquad (2.15)$$

Similarly, differentiating Equation (2.14) with respect to y gives

$$2g(x)k'(y) + p'(y) = 0$$

$$\frac{p'(y)}{k'(y)} + 2g(x) = 0$$

Hence the following must be true:

$$g(x) = -\gamma^2 = \text{constant} \qquad (2.16)$$

Case I. $k(y) = -\lambda^2$

Case Ia. $\lambda^2 > 0$

$$k(y) = \frac{Y''}{Y} = -\lambda^2$$

$$Y'' + \lambda^2 Y = 0$$

$$\therefore \quad Y = \left\{ \begin{array}{c} \cos\lambda y \\ \sin\lambda y \end{array} \right\} \qquad (2.17a)$$

Substituting Equation (2.15) into Equation (2.13) gives

$$\frac{X^{IV}}{X} - 2\lambda^2 \frac{X''}{X} + \lambda^4 = 0$$

$$X^{IV} - 2\lambda^2 X'' + \lambda^4 X = 0$$

Let $X = e^{\alpha x}$

$$\alpha^4 - 2\lambda^2\alpha^2 + \lambda^4 = 0 = (\alpha^2 - \lambda^2)^2$$

$$\therefore \quad \alpha = \pm\lambda, \pm\lambda$$

$$X = \left\{ \begin{array}{c} \cosh\lambda x \\ x\cosh\lambda x \\ \sinh\lambda x \\ x\sinh\lambda x \end{array} \right\} \qquad (2.17b)$$

So we have eight such products as solutions of $\nabla^4 w = 0$,

where $w(x,y) = X(x)Y(y)$ and $k(y) = -\lambda^2$.

Case Ib. $\lambda^2 = 0$

$$k(y) = \frac{Y''}{Y} = 0$$

$$Y = \left\{ \begin{array}{c} 1 \\ y \end{array} \right\} \tag{2.18a}$$

Substituting Equation (2.15) into Equation (2.13) gives

$$\frac{X^{IV}}{X} - 2\lambda^2 \frac{X''}{X} + \lambda^4 = 0$$

$$X^{IV} - 2\lambda^2 X'' + \lambda^4 X = 0$$

If $\lambda^2 = 0$,

$$X^{IV} = 0$$

$$X = \left\{ \begin{array}{c} 1 \\ x \\ x^2 \\ x^3 \end{array} \right\} \tag{2.18b}$$

Hence another eight products are found to be solutions to $\nabla^4 w = 0$,

where $w = X(x)Y(y)$ and $k(y) = 0$.

Case Ic. $\lambda^2 < 0$

Here λ is imaginary; hence let $\lambda = i\bar{\lambda}$.

$$Y'' + \lambda^2 Y = 0 = Y'' - \bar{\lambda}^2 Y = 0$$

$$Y = \left\{ \begin{array}{c} \sinh \bar{\lambda} y \\ \cosh \bar{\lambda} y \end{array} \right\} \tag{2.19a}$$

As before, $\alpha = \pm \lambda, \pm \lambda$, where λ is imaginary. Let $X = e^{\alpha x}$

$$\frac{X^{IV}}{X} - 2\lambda^2 \frac{X''}{X} + \lambda^4 = 0$$

$$\alpha^4 + 2\bar{\lambda}^2 \alpha^2 + \bar{\lambda}^4 = 0$$

$$(\alpha^2 + \bar{\lambda}^2)(\alpha^2 + \bar{\lambda}^2) = 0, \qquad \alpha = \pm i\bar{\lambda}, \pm i\bar{\lambda}$$

$$X = \left\{ \begin{array}{c} \cos \bar{\lambda} x \\ x \cos \bar{\lambda} x \\ \sin \bar{\lambda} x \\ x \sin \bar{\lambda} x \end{array} \right\} \qquad (2.19b)$$

Case II. $g(x) = -\gamma^2$

Case IIa. $\gamma^2 > 0$

$$g(x) = \frac{X''}{X} = -\gamma^2 \qquad (2.20)$$

$$X'' + \gamma^2 X = 0$$

$$X = \left\{ \begin{array}{c} \cos \gamma x \\ \sin \gamma x \end{array} \right\} \qquad (2.21a)$$

and as before,

$$Y = \left\{ \begin{array}{c} \cosh \gamma y \\ y \cosh \gamma y \\ \sinh \gamma y \\ y \sinh \gamma y \end{array} \right\} \qquad (2.21b)$$

Case IIb. $\gamma^2 = 0$

$$X = \left\{ \begin{array}{c} 1 \\ x \end{array} \right\} \qquad (2.22)$$

$$Y = \left\{ \begin{array}{c} 1 \\ y \\ y^2 \\ y^3 \end{array} \right\}$$

Case IIc. $\gamma^2 < 0$

Let $\gamma = i\bar{\gamma}$.

$$X = \left\{ \begin{array}{c} \cosh \bar{\gamma} x \\ \sinh \bar{\gamma} x \end{array} \right\} \tag{2.23}$$

$$Y = \left\{ \begin{array}{c} \sin \bar{\gamma} y \\ y \sin \bar{\gamma} y \\ \cos \bar{\gamma} y \\ y \cos \bar{\gamma} y \end{array} \right\}$$

So there are eight possible products to satisfy each particular case. These solutions comprise all the possible separable solutions of the homogeneous biharmonic equation. One can attempt to find the solution of any particular problem by exploiting the boundary conditions and loading, intuition, and experience. However, if that fails, then one can resort to trying each of the above solutions.

2.3   DOUBLE-SERIES SOLUTION (NAVIER SOLUTION)

In plate problems one can usually obtain solutions using a doubly infinite series, such as

$$w(x,y) = \sum_{m=1}^{\infty} \sum_{n=1}^{\infty} A_{mn} f_m(x) g_n(y)$$

But such solutions are often miserable to compute because of their slow convergence. Instead one usually tries to obtain a solution where the function of only one spatial variable is summed for, so that

$$w(x,y) = \sum_{n=1}^{\infty} \phi_n(y) f_n(x)$$

This approach is particularly useful when two opposite edges are simply supported, because then the function $f_n(x)$ above can be a half-range sine series.

In assuming the functions $f_m(x)$ and $g_n(y)$ for the double-series solution (Navier solution), or assuming the functions $f_n(x)$ for the single-series solution (Levy solution), these functions must be complete in order that the lateral deflection can be adequately represented. Furthermore it is most convenient from a computational point of view that the functions be orthogonal. Also, of course, they must satisfy the boundary conditions for the problem. One straightforward approach to selecting such functions is to use the vibration modes or buckling modes for a beam of constant cross section with the same boundary conditions as those on opposite edges of the plate, because all such modes comprise a complete, orthogonal set. The beam vibration modes for all boundary conditions and their properties have been conveniently catalogued by Young and Felgar[1] and by Felgar.[2]

The double-infinite-series approach is treated first. Consider a rectangular plate simply supported on all four edges in the region $0 \leqslant x \leqslant a$, $0 \leqslant y \leqslant b$, $-h/2 \leqslant z \leqslant h/2$. The governing equation is

$$\nabla^4 w = \frac{p(x,y)}{D}$$

The solution can be written as

$$w(x,y) = \sum_{m=1}^{\infty} \sum_{n=1}^{\infty} A_{mn} \sin \frac{m\pi x}{a} \sin \frac{n\pi y}{b} \qquad (2.24)$$

because these functions are complete and they satisfy the boundary conditions of the problem. The lateral load must be expanded in the same kind of series:

$$p(x,y) = \sum_{m=1}^{\infty} \sum_{n=1}^{\infty} B_{mn} \sin \frac{m\pi x}{a} \sin \frac{n\pi y}{b} \qquad (2.25)$$

where $\quad B_{mn} = \frac{4}{ab} \int_0^a \int_0^b p(x,y) \sin \frac{m\pi x}{a} \sin \frac{n\pi y}{b} \, dy \, dx$

Substituting these series representations of the load and lateral deflection into the governing differential equation, we obtain

$$\sum \sum A_{mn} \pi^4 \left\{ \frac{m^4}{a^4} + 2\frac{m^2}{a^2}\frac{n^2}{b^2} + \frac{n^4}{b^4} \right\} \sin \frac{m\pi x}{a} \sin \frac{n\pi y}{b}$$

$$= \frac{1}{D} \sum \sum B_{mn} \sin \frac{m\pi x}{a} \sin \frac{n\pi y}{b} \qquad (2.26)$$

For these doubly infinite series to be equal requires that an equality exist for each combination of m and n in the series. By looking at the mth and nth term, A_{mn} is easily found in terms of B_{mn}.

$$A_{mn} = \frac{B_{mn}}{D\pi^4 \left\{ \dfrac{m^2}{a^2} + \dfrac{n^2}{b^2} \right\}^2}$$

Thus the solution is easily found for this case, because B_{mn} is determined from Equation (2.25), and A_{mn} is then found from the equation above; hence $w(x,y)$ is then known everywhere from Equation (2.24). From this, all slopes, stress couples, and shear resultants can be calculated at any location (x,y). As mentioned previously, the doubly-infinite-series solution usually converges slowly. Moreover, the derivatives of $w(x,y)$ needed to obtain stress couples and shear resultants always converge still more slowly than the function itself.

An example of obtaining B_{mn} can be briefly given. Consider a plate simply supported on all four edges and subjected to a uniform constant lateral loading p_0.

$$B_{mn} = \frac{4p_0}{ab} \int_0^a \int_0^b \sin\frac{m\pi x}{a} \sin\frac{n\pi y}{b} \, dy \, dx$$

$$= \frac{4p_0}{ab} \left\{ \frac{a}{m\pi} \left[-\cos\frac{m\pi x}{a} \right]_0^a \right\} \left\{ \frac{b}{n\pi} \left[-\cos\frac{n\pi y}{b} \right]_0^b \right\}$$

$$= \frac{4p_0}{mn\pi^2} (1 - \cos m\pi)(1 - \cos n\pi)$$

$$= \frac{4p_0}{mn\pi^2} [1 - (-1)^m][1 - (-1)^n]$$

$$= \frac{16p_0}{mn\pi^2} \qquad (m,n \text{ odd only})$$

2.4 SINGLE-SERIES SOLUTION (LEVY SOLUTION)

Consider a plate with opposite edges simply supported, as shown in Sketch 2.3. Again, the governing differential equation is

$$\nabla^4 w = \frac{p(x,y)}{D}$$

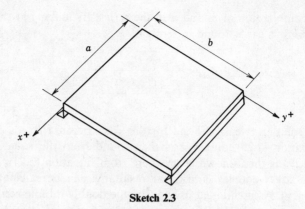

Sketch 2.3

The boundary conditions on the y edges are

$$w(x,0) = w(x,b) = 0$$

$$M_y(x,0) = M_y(x,b) = 0 \qquad (2.27)$$

From Equation (1.50), the stress couple is given by

$$M_y = -D\left[\frac{\partial^2 w}{\partial y^2} + \nu\frac{\partial^2 w}{\partial x^2}\right].$$

Hence on the $y=0$ and $y=b$ edges,

$$\frac{\partial^2 w}{\partial y^2}\left(x, \begin{matrix}0\\b\end{matrix}\right) + \nu\frac{\partial^2 w}{\partial x^2}\left(x, \begin{matrix}0\\b\end{matrix}\right) = 0$$

However, $\dfrac{\partial^2 w}{\partial x^2}\left(x, \begin{matrix}0\\b\end{matrix}\right) = 0$ because the curvature is zero parallel to the simply supported edge. Therefore,

$$\frac{\partial^2 w}{\partial y^2}\left(x, \begin{matrix}0\\b\end{matrix}\right) = 0.$$

Assume a form of the solution to be the following, which satisfies the boundary condition on the y edges given by Equation (2.27):

$$w(x,y) = \sum_{n=1}^{\infty} \phi_n(x) \sin\frac{n\pi y}{b}. \qquad (2.28)$$

For this example, the lateral pressure is taken to be

$$p(x,y) = g(x)h(y) \tag{2.29}$$

where $g(x)$ and $h(y)$ are known. It is necessary to expand $h(y)$ in a series solution corresponding to (2.28). Hence

$$h(y) = \sum_{n=1}^{\infty} A_n \sin \frac{n\pi y}{b} \tag{2.30}$$

where $A_n = \dfrac{2}{b} \displaystyle\int_0^b h(y) \sin \frac{n\pi y}{b} \, dy$

Substituting Equations (2.28) and (2.29) into (2.26) gives

$$\sum_{n=1}^{\infty} \left\{ \phi_n^{IV} - 2\lambda_n^2 \phi_n'' + \lambda_n^4 \phi_n \right\} \sin \frac{n\pi y}{b} = \frac{1}{D} \sum_{n=1}^{\infty} A_n g_n(x) \sin \frac{n\pi y}{b} \tag{2.31}$$

where $\lambda_n = n\pi / b$.

For this to be true, the series must be equal term by term:

$$\phi_n^{IV}(x) - 2\lambda_n^2 \phi_n''(x) + \lambda_n^4 \phi_n(x) = \frac{1}{D} A_n g_n(x) \tag{2.32}$$

Note: We have arrived at this point without specifying any boundary conditions on the other two edges. Hence, whenever a problem has two opposite edges simply supported, one can arrive at Equation (2.32) without any other information.

Case I

Now let $x = 0$, a be simply supported edges; let $p(x,y)$ be a function of y only, hence $g(x) = 1$. The boundary conditions are

$$w(0,y) = 0, \qquad w(a,y) = 0$$

$$M_x(0,y) = 0, \qquad M_x(a,y) = 0$$

So

$$\frac{\partial^2 w}{\partial x^2} \begin{pmatrix} 0 \\ a \end{pmatrix} , y = 0$$

Now since

$$w(x,y) = \sum_{n=1}^{\infty} \phi_n(x) \sin \frac{n\pi y}{b}$$

$$\phi_n(0) = \phi_n(a) = 0 \tag{2.33}$$

$$\phi_n''(0) = \phi_n''(a) = 0$$

and Equation (2.32) becomes

$$\phi_n^{IV} - 2\lambda_n^2 \phi_n'' + \lambda_n^4 \phi_n = \frac{A_n}{D} \tag{2.34}$$

From Equation (2.34) we must now solve for ϕ_n. Proceeding in the customary, to obtain the complementary solution we let $\phi_n = e^{sx}$

$$s^4 - 2\lambda_n^2 s^2 + \lambda_n^4 = 0$$

$$(s^2 - \lambda_n^2)(s^2 - \lambda_n^2) = 0 \qquad \text{where } \lambda_n^2 > 0$$

$$s = \pm \lambda_n, \pm \lambda_n$$

So the complementary solution is

$$\phi_n(x) = (C_1 + C_2 x)\cosh \lambda_n x + (C_3 + C_4 x)\sinh \lambda_n x$$

The particular solution is easily seen to be $\phi_n = A_n/D\lambda_n^4$. The complete solution for $\phi_n(x)$ therefore is

$$\phi_n(x) = (C_1 + C_2 x)\cosh \lambda_n x + (C_3 + C_4 x)\sinh \lambda_n x + \frac{A_n}{D\lambda_n^4} \tag{2.35}$$

Equation (2.35) is the form of the solution for $\phi_n(x)$ for any set of boundary conditions on the $x = 0$, $x = a$ edges. For loads that are a function of x the particular solution of course will differ from that of Equation (2.35). Substituting Equation (2.35) [the complete solution for $\phi_n(x)$] and its derivatives into Equation (2.33) [the boundary conditions on the x edges] provides the values of the undetermined constants C_1 through C_4 for this problem. The results are:

$$C_1 = -\frac{A_n}{D\lambda_n^4}$$

$$C_2 = \frac{A_n}{2D\lambda_n^3}\frac{(1-\cosh\lambda_n a)}{\sinh\lambda_n a} \tag{2.36}$$

$$C_3 = \frac{A_n a}{2D\lambda_n^3(1+\cosh\lambda_n a)}\left[\frac{2}{\lambda_n a}\sinh\lambda_n a - 1\right]$$

$$C_4 = \frac{A_n}{2D\lambda_n^3}$$

Thus, the complete solution for the lateral deflection is

$$w(x,y) = \sum_{n=1}^{\infty}\left[(C_1+C_2x)\cosh\lambda_n x + (C_3+C_4x)\sinh\lambda_n x + \frac{A_n}{D\lambda_n^4}\right]\sin\lambda_n y \tag{2.37}$$

where C_1 through C_4 are given by (2.36).

It should be noted that we could have solved this problem by expressing the deflection any one of the following ways:

$$w(x,y) = \sum_{m=1}^{\infty}\sum_{n=1}^{\infty} A_{mn}\sin\frac{m\pi x}{a}\sin\frac{n\pi y}{b}$$

$$w(x,y) = \sum_{n=1}^{\infty}\phi_n(x)\sin\frac{n\pi y}{b}$$

$$w(x,y) = \sum_{m=1}^{\infty}\psi_m(y)\sin\frac{m\pi x}{a}$$

The first of these series converges more slowly, while the second and third converge quite rapidly.

For the case of the x edges being clamped or free, and with the same loading $[p=p(y)$ only], Equation (2.35) with the appropriate boundary conditions may be used to obtain the solution.

2.5 EXAMPLE OF A PLATE WITH EDGES SUPPORTED BY BEAMS

Consider a rectangular plate (Sketch 2.4) with the following boundary conditions:

$$y = 0, b \qquad \text{simply supported}$$

$$x = 0, a \qquad \text{supported by beams}$$

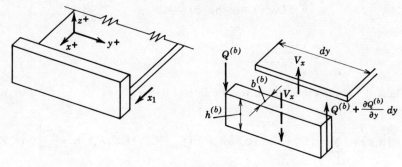

Sketch 2.4

and a lateral load given by

$$p(x,y) = \sum_{n=1}^{\infty} A_n \sin \frac{n\pi y}{b}$$

For one boundary condition on the x edge, consider an element of beam as a free body, as shown above. A force balance in the z direction provides one plate boundary condition.

In the sketch the quantities with superscript b refer to a beam, whose flexural stiffness is $(EI)^b$, and which is mechanically joined to the edge of the plate denoted by $x = x_1$ in such a way that the middle surfaces of the plate and beam are identical (to retain simplicity in this example). Hence the lateral deflections of the beam and plate are identical at their common boundary, $x = x_1$. Therefore, the force balance is given by the following, where the shear resultant of the beam is

$$Q_y^{(b)}(y) = b^{(b)} \int_{-h^{(b)}/2}^{+h^{(b)}/2} \sigma_{yz} \, dz$$

and the Kirchoff "effective" shear resultant is used for the plate:

$$\sum F_z^{(b)} = 0 = -Q^{(b)} - V_x \, dy + Q^{(b)} + \frac{dQ^{(b)}}{dy} \, dy = 0$$

$$(V_x)_{x=x_1} = \frac{dQ^{(b)}}{dy}(x_1,y) = -(EI)^{(b)}\left(\frac{\partial^4 w^{(b)}}{\partial y^4}\right)_{x=x_1} = -(EI)^b\left(\frac{\partial^4 w}{\partial y^4}\right)_{x=x_1}$$

since $w_b = w$ at $x = x_1$, $Q^{(b)} = dM^{(b)}/dy$, and $M^{(b)} = -(EI)^{(b)}\partial^2 w^{(b)}/\partial y^2$.
For the plate,

$$(V_x)_{x=x_1} = -D\left[\frac{\partial^3 w}{\partial x^3} + (2-\nu)\frac{\partial^3 w}{\partial x \partial y^2}\right]_{x=x_1}$$

The second boundary condition is provided by the balancing of twisting moments (Sketch 2.5). The beam has a torsional stiffness $(GJ)^b$.

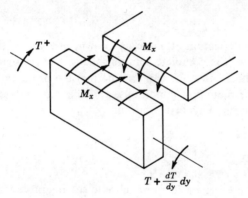

Sketch 2.5

For the beam, at $x = x_1$,

$$-T - M_x \, dy + T + \frac{dT}{dy} \, dy = 0$$

$$M_x = \frac{dT}{dy} = -(GJ)^b\frac{d^2\theta^{(b)}}{dy^2} = -(GJ)^b\left(\frac{\partial^3 w}{\partial x \partial y^2}\right) = -D\left[\frac{\partial^2 w}{\partial x^2} + \nu\frac{\partial^2 w}{\partial y^2}\right]$$

where

$$T = -(GJ)^b\frac{d\theta^{(b)}}{dy} \quad \text{and} \quad \theta = \frac{\partial w^{(b)}}{\partial x}$$

and

$$\frac{dw^{(b)}}{dx} = \frac{dw}{dx} \quad \text{at } x = x_1$$

So the boundary conditions are

$$D\left[\frac{\partial^3 w}{\partial x^3} + (2-\nu)\frac{\partial^3 w}{\partial x \partial y^2}\right] = (EI)^b \frac{\partial^4 w}{\partial y^4} \quad \text{at } x = x_1 \qquad (2.38)$$

$$D\left[\frac{\partial^2 w}{\partial x^2} + \nu\frac{\partial^2 w}{\partial y^2}\right] = (GJ)^b \frac{\partial^3 w}{\partial x \partial y^2} \quad \text{at } x = x_1 \qquad (2.39)$$

Once the plate deflection at $x = x_1$ is known, one knows the deflection of the beam, and so the complete solution of the beam is determined also.

For all practical cases one can assume that the beam end conditions are the same as the plate end conditions, and that the ends of the beam are completely restrained against rotation.

2.6 SUMMARY

In this chapter the two basic approaches to solving problems of rectangular plates subjected to lateral loads have been treated. In addition the behavior of plates subjected only to pure bending was studied to obtain a physical insight into both synclastic and anticlastic bending. Finally, a more complicated boundary-condition example was investigated than the classical boundary conditions of Chapter 1. In rectangular plates with more difficult boundary conditions than simply supported edges, references 1 and 2 provide functions suitable for either the Navier or the Levy method.

Many solutions to plate problems are known, and are catalogued in numerous works such as those of Timoshenko and Woinowsky-Krieger,[3] Marguerre and Woernle,[4] and Mansfield.[5]

Methods of analysis are developed and solutions are given for rectangular plates of anisotropic materials and composite materials in a text by Vinson and Chou.[6]

2.7 REFERENCES

1. D. Young and R. P. Felgar, Jr., *Tables of Characteristic Functions Representing Normal Modes of Vibration of a Beam*, The University of Texas Engineering Research Series Report No. 44, July 1, 1949.
2. R. P. Felgar, Jr., *Formulas for Integrals Containing Characteristic Functions of a Vibrating Beam*, The University of Texas Bureau of Engineering Research Circular No. 14, 1950.
3. S. Timoshenko and A. Woinowsky-Krieger, *Theory of Plates and Shells*, 2nd ed., McGraw-Hill, 1959.
4. K. Marguerre and H. T. Woernle, *Elastic Plates*, Blaisdell, 1970.
5. E. H. Mansfield, *The Bending and Stretching of Plates*, Pergamon, 1964.
6. J. R. Vinson and T. W. Chou, *Composite Materials and Their Use in Structures*, Applied Science Publishers. 1974.

2.8 PROBLEMS

2.1. Consider a rectangular isotropic plate occupying the region $0 \leqslant x \leqslant a$, $0 \leqslant y \leqslant b$, $-h/2 \leqslant z \leqslant h/2$. The plate is simply supported on the edges $y = 0$ and b. It is subjected to a laterally distributed load given by Equations (2.29) and (2.30). If $g(x) = 1$, the solution is given by Equation (2.37). If the plate is clamped along the edges $x = 0$ and a, determine C_1 through C_4.

2.2. In Problem 2.1, if the plate is free along the edges $x = 0$ and a, determine the constants C_1 through C_4.

2.3. In Problem 2.1, if the plate is simply supported at $x = 0$ and clamped at $x = a$, determine the constants C_1 through C_4.

2.4. In Problem 2.1, if the plate is simply supported at $x = 0$ and free along $x = a$, determine the constants C_1 through C_4.

2.5. In Problem 2.1, if the plate is clamped along $x = a$ and free along $x = 0$, determine the constants C_1 through C_4.

2.6. Consider a floor slab whose geometry is as described in Problem 2.1. The slab is square, simply supported on all edges, and loaded with sand in such a way that the load can be approximated by

$$p(x,y) = p_0 \sin \frac{\pi x}{a} \sin \frac{\pi y}{b}$$

Determine the location and magnitude of the maximum deflection, the maximum bending stresses in each direction, and the maximum shear stresses in each direction.

2.7. A certain window in an aircraft is approximated by a square plate of dimension a on each side, simply supported on all four edges and subjected to a uniform cabin pressure p_0. Using the Navier solution for a square plate of length and width a, the solution is given by Equation (2.24). The maximum value of the lateral deflection can be written as

$$w_{max} = C_1 \frac{p_0 a^4}{D}$$

for a plate subjected to a constant lateral loading p_0. Determine the numerical coefficient C_1 to three significant figures.

The maximum bending moment $M_{x\,max} = M_{y\,max}$ can be written as

$$M_{max} = C_2 p_0 a^2$$

Find C_2 to three significant figures, if the Poisson's ratio of the window material is $\nu = 0.3$.

2.8. A certain hull plate on the flat bottom of a ship may be considered to be a rectangular plate under uniform loading p_0 from the water pressure, and clamped along all edges. A $\frac{1}{2}$-in. steel plate 4 ft in width is to be used for the bottom plate. The ship draws $13\frac{1}{2}$ ft of water maximum. If the maximum allowable stress in the steel is 20,000 psi, what is the maximum plate length (i.e., bulkhead spacing) that can be used in the ship design, and what is the corresponding maximum deflection of the hull plate? Salt water weighs 64 lb/ft^3, $E_{steel} = 30 \times 10^6$ psi, and $\nu_{steel} = 0.3$.

For a plate clamped on all four edges, subjected to a lateral load p_0, the maximum deflection and maximum stress couple can be written as

$$w_{max} = \frac{C_1 p_0 a^4}{E h^3} \qquad \text{where } \nu = 0.3$$

$$M_{max} = M_{x\,max} = C_2 p_0 a^2 \qquad \text{where } \nu = 0.3$$

Then the following values of C_1 and C_2 can be calculated for various plate aspect ratios b/a:

b/a	1.0	1.2	1.4	1.6	1.8	2.0	∞
C_1	0.0138	0.0188	0.0226	0.0251	0.0267	0.0277	0.0285
C_2	0.0513	0.0639	0.0726	0.0780	0.0812	0.0829	0.0833

Linear interpolation is permitted.

2.9.   A rectangular wing-panel component, 8 in. $\times$ 5 in., is made of aluminum, and under the most severe maneuver conditions can be subjected to a uniform lateral load of 20 psi. This wing panel can be approximated by a flat plate simply supported on all four edges. What thickness must the panel have, and what is the resulting maximum deflection under this maneuver condition?

If a rectangular plate is simply supported on all four edges and subjected to uniform lateral load, with $\nu = 0.3$, then the maximum deflection w_{max} and the maximum moment $M_x = M_{max}$, located at $(x = a/2, y = b/2)$, can be expressed as

$$w_{max} = \frac{C_1 p_0 a^4}{Eh^3}$$

$$M_{max} = M_{x\,max} = C_2 p_0 a^2$$

The resulting values of C_1 and C_2 are:

b/a	1.0	1.2	1.4	1.6	1.8	2.0	3.0	4.0	5.0	∞
C_1	0.044	0.062	0.077	0.091	0.102	0.111	0.134	0.140	0.142	0.142
C_2	0.048	0.063	0.075	0.086	0.095	0.102	0.119	0.124	0.125	0.125

The aluminum used has an allowable stress of 20,000 psi; it has $E = 10 \times 10^6$ psi and $\nu = 0.3$.

2.10.   A rectangular steel plate is used as part of a flood-control structure, and it is mounted vertically under water so that it is subjected to a hydraulic loading

$$p(x,y) = p_0 + p_1 \frac{y}{b}$$

where p_0 and p_1 are constants associated with the pressure heads. Find the Euler coefficient B_{mn} in Equation (2.25) for this loading.

2.11.   A glass manufacturer has been asked to construct plate-glass windows for a new modern office building. They must be 10 ft wide and 20 ft high. Design the windows so that they can withstand wind forces due to air velocities of 150 mi/hr. State all assumptions and physical constants clearly.

2.12. A flat portion of a wind tunnel measuring 30 in. × 54 in. is to be subjected to a maximum uniform wind load of 10 psi. If the steel to be used has an allowable stress of 40,000 psi, and a Poisson's ratio $v = 0.3$, what plate thickness is required if the plate is

(a) Simply supported on all four edges?

(b) Clamped on all four edges?

Use the data from Problems 2.8 and 2.9.

2.13. A portion of the cover on a hovercraft is to be rectangular measuring 8 ft × 4 ft in planform, and is to be simply supported on all four edges. It is calculated that the maximum air pressure the panel will be subjected to is 20 psi.

(a) How thick must the panel be if it is constructed of aluminum ($E = 10 \times 10^6$ psi, $v = 0.3$) and if the allowable stress is limited to 30,000 psi?

(b) How thick must the plate be if it is constructed of steel ($E = 30 \times 10^6$ psi, $v = 0.3$) and if the allowable stress is limited to 60,000 psi?

(c) If the weight density of steel is 0.283 lb/in.^{3} and that of aluminum is 0.1 lb/in.^{3}, which material should be selected to minimize weight?

(d) Suppose the aluminum plate of (a) above were clamped on all four edges; what thickness would be required?

Use the data of Problems 2.8 and 2.9.

3

THERMAL STRESSES IN PLATES

3.1. GENERAL CONSIDERATIONS

Consider any elastic body with a constant coefficient of thermal expansion, γ, in units of in./(in.)(°F), or equivalent, at a uniform temperature at which the body is assumed to be free of thermal stresses and strains. If the body is free to deform, and the temperature is raised slowly to T degrees above the stress-free temperature, the thermal strains produced at any material point can be written as

$$\varepsilon_{ij\,\text{th}} = \gamma T(x_i)\delta_{ij} \tag{3.1}$$

where x_i are the coordinate directions, and δ_{ij} is the Kronecker delta ($\delta_{ij} = 1$ for $i = j$, $= 0$ for $i \neq j$). It should be noted that thermal strains are purely dilitational ($i = j$); thermal shear strains do not exist.

In Equation (3.1), T is positive when the temperature at the material point is above the stress-free temperature. The coefficient of thermal expansion, γ, is positive for all isotropic engineering materials; that is, the body expands when it is heated.

In many thermoelastic bodies the changes in internal temperature tend to result in strains that do not satisfy the compatibility equations. In that case isothermal strains $\varepsilon_{ij\,\text{iso}}$ (the strains discussed in Chapter 1) are induced, such that the total strain $\varepsilon_{ij\,\text{tot}}$ satisfies compatibility.

$$\varepsilon_{ij\,\text{tot}} = \varepsilon_{ij\,\text{iso}} + \varepsilon_{ij\,\text{th}} \tag{3.2}$$

In that case the "thermal stresses" are due to the isothermal strains induced to ensure compatibility.

A second way that thermal stresses occur is through displacement restrictions on the elastic body. One simple example of this occurs when a bar is placed between immovable end grips and subsequently heated. There, compressive thermal stresses result.

Thus, thermal stresses are caused by two mechanisms: displacement restrictions, and induced isothermal strains required for compatibility.

Next, consider a thin rod at a uniform temperature. If the rod is slowly and uniformly heated, so that the thermal strains satisfy the compatibility equations, the heated rod has thermal strains but no thermal stresses. Now if the unheated thin rod is placed in immovable end grips such that the rod cannot increase in length, slow uniform heating results in thermal stresses but no thermal strains.

In the latter case, if the compressive axial thermal stresses reach a value equal to the Euler buckling load (discussed in Chapter 5), the rod buckles. This is called thermal buckling.

3.2. DERIVATION OF THE GOVERNING EQUATIONS FOR A THERMOELASTIC PLATE

In deriving the governing equations for a thermoelastic plate, the equilibrium equations and the strain-displacement equations are not altered from those of the isothermal plate of Chapter 1, because the former equations involve force balances, whereas the latter are purely kinematical relationships involving total strains.

Thus the stress-strain relations, Equations (1.4) and (1.5), are modified in accordance with Equations (3.2) and (3.1):

$$\varepsilon_{x\,\text{iso}} = \varepsilon_{x\,\text{tot}} - \gamma T = \frac{1}{E}\left[\sigma_x - \nu\sigma_y\right]$$

$$\varepsilon_{y\,\text{iso}} = \varepsilon_{y\,\text{tot}} - \gamma T = \frac{1}{E}\left[\sigma_y - \nu\sigma_x\right]$$

or

$$\varepsilon_x = \frac{1}{E}\left[\sigma_x - \nu\sigma_y\right] + \gamma T \tag{3.4}$$

$$\varepsilon_y = \frac{1}{E}\left[\sigma_y - \nu\sigma_x\right] + \gamma T \tag{3.5}$$

In Equations (3.4) and (3.5) and in all that follows, the subscript for total strains is dropped, and all strains mentioned explicitly are those that satisfy compatibility, and that appear in the strain-displacement relations. Hence in Equations (3.4) and (3.5), the first terms on the right-hand side are really the isothermal strains, and the second terms on the right-hand side are thermal strains.

We proceed as in Chapter 1, employing the strain-displacement relations, Equations (1.10) and (1.11). Equations (3.4) and (3.5) after multiplication by E become

$$\sigma_x - \nu\sigma_y + E\gamma T = E\frac{\partial u_0}{\partial x} - Ez\frac{\partial^2 w}{\partial x^2} \tag{3.6}$$

$$\sigma_y - \nu\sigma_x + E\gamma T = E\frac{\partial v_0}{\partial y} - Ez\frac{\partial^2 w}{\partial y^2} \tag{3.7}$$

We now define two quantities N^* and M^*, known as the thermal stress resultant and the thermal stress couple, respectively:

$$N^* = \int_{-h/2}^{+h/2} E\gamma T\,dz, \quad M^* = \int_{-h/2}^{+h/2} E\gamma Tz\,dz \tag{3.8}$$

Multiplying Equations (3.6) and (3.7) by dz and integrating across the thickness of the plate, then multiplying them by $z\,dz$ and similarly integrating them, we obtain the integrated stress-strain relations for a thermoelastic plate. It should be remembered from the discussion in Section 3.1 that the shear stress-strain relations are not altered by the inclusion of thermoelastic effects.

$$N_x - \nu N_y + N^* = Eh \frac{\partial u_0}{\partial x}$$

$$N_y - \nu N_x + N^* = Eh \frac{\partial v_0}{\partial y}$$

$$M_x - \nu M_y + M^* = - \frac{Eh^3}{12} \frac{\partial^2 w}{\partial x^2}$$

$$M_y - \nu M_x + M^* = - \frac{Eh^3}{12} \frac{\partial^2 w}{\partial y^2}$$

$$N_{xy} = \frac{K(1-\nu)}{2} \left[\frac{\partial u_0}{\partial y} + \frac{\partial v_0}{\partial x} \right] \tag{3.9}$$

$$M_{xy} = - D(1-\nu) \frac{\partial^2 w}{\partial x \partial y} \tag{3.10}$$

Rearranging the first four of the above results in

$$N_x = K \left[\frac{\partial u_0}{\partial x} + \nu \frac{\partial v_0}{\partial y} \right] - \frac{N^*}{1-\nu} \tag{3.11}$$

$$N_y = K \left[\frac{\partial v_0}{\partial y} + \nu \frac{\partial u_0}{\partial x} \right] - \frac{N^*}{1-\nu} \tag{3.12}$$

$$M_x = - D \left[\frac{\partial^2 w}{\partial x^2} + \nu \frac{\partial^2 w}{\partial y^2} \right] - \frac{M^*}{1-\nu} \tag{3.13}$$

$$M_y = - D \left[\frac{\partial^2 w}{\partial y^2} + \nu \frac{\partial^2 w}{\partial x^2} \right] - \frac{M^*}{1-\nu} \tag{3.14}$$

By introducing these thermoelastic stress-strain relations into the equilibrium equations (1.62) through (1.64) and (1.68) and (1.69), the governing differential equations for a thermoelastic plate are determined.

$$D\nabla^4 w = p(x,y) - \frac{1}{1-\nu}\nabla^2 M^* \qquad (3.15)$$

$$K\nabla^4 u_0 = \frac{1}{1-\nu}\frac{\partial}{\partial x}(\nabla^2 N^*) \qquad (3.16)$$

$$K\nabla^4 v_0 = \frac{1}{1-\nu}\frac{\partial}{\partial y}(\nabla^2 N^*) \qquad (3.17)$$

It should be noted that if there are surface shear stresses τ_{1x}, τ_{2x}, τ_{1y}, and τ_{2y} acting on the plate, the terms resulting from Problem1.1 also have to be added to the right-hand sides of Equations (3.15) through (3.17).

For completeness, some other useful relationships are catalogued below:

$$Q_x = -D\frac{\partial}{\partial x}(\nabla^2 w) - \frac{1}{1-\nu}\frac{\partial M^*}{\partial x}$$
$$ \qquad (3.18)$$
$$Q_y = -D\frac{\partial}{\partial y}(\nabla^2 w) - \frac{1}{1-\nu}\frac{\partial M^*}{\partial y}$$

$$V_x = -D\left[\frac{\partial^3 w}{\partial x^3} + (2-\nu)\frac{\partial^3 w}{\partial x\partial y^2}\right] - \frac{1}{1-\nu}\frac{\partial M^*}{\partial x}$$
$$ \qquad (3.19)$$
$$V_y = -D\left[\frac{\partial^3 w}{\partial y^3} + (2-\nu)\frac{\partial^3 w}{\partial y\partial x^2}\right] - \frac{1}{1-\nu}\frac{\partial M^*}{\partial y}$$

With the inclusion of thermal quantities, the expressions for various normal stresses in the plate are modified as follows:

$$\sigma_x = \frac{1}{h}\left[N_x + \frac{N^*}{1-\nu}\right] + \frac{z}{h^3/12}\left[M_x + \frac{M^*}{1-\nu}\right] - \frac{E\gamma T}{1-\nu}$$
$$ \qquad (3.20)$$
$$\sigma_y = \frac{1}{h}\left[N_y + \frac{N^*}{1-\nu}\right] + \frac{z}{h^3/12}\left[M_y + \frac{M^*}{1-\nu}\right] - \frac{E\gamma T}{1-\nu}$$

The inclusion of the N^* and M^* terms is easy to understand, since they are thermal-stress resultants and couples analogous to N_x, N_y, M_x, and M_y, which are caused by lateral and in-plane "mechanical" loads. The last terms in Equation (3.20) can be understood physically through the following example, in which we assume that the first two terms do not contribute. Suppose, at some value of (x,y) in a plate, the upper surface is heated while the lower surface is cooled. Thus the value of T in the upper portion of the plate is positive and becomes negative in the lower plate portion, as shown in Sketch 3.1 below. The last term of Equation (3.20) shows that there are compressive stresses in the upper portion of the plate, while in the lower portion there are tensile stresses. Intuitively the material points in the upper portion of the plate "want" to expand considerably but are restrained by those in the cooler areas of the plate, so that there are compressive stresses there. Likewise, in the cooler portion of the plate the material points "want" to contract, but are extended by the hotter portions of the plate, and hence put under tension. Such thermal stresses can result in material failure, just as stresses caused by mechanical loads do.

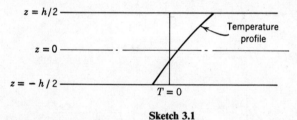

Sketch 3.1

As mentioned before, shear stress and strains are not affected by thermal effects, and hence remain the same as in Chapter 1:

$$\sigma_{xy} = \frac{N_{xy}}{h} + \frac{M_{xy}z}{h^3/12}$$

$$\sigma_{xz} = \frac{3Q_x}{2h}\left[1 - \left(\frac{z}{h/2}\right)^2\right] \tag{3.21}$$

$$\sigma_{yz} = \frac{3Q_y}{2h}\left[1 - \left(\frac{z}{h/2}\right)^2\right]$$

Of course, if there exist shear stresses on the upper or lower surface of the plate, the last two expressions must be modified as in Chapter 1.

To obtain solutions for thermoelastic plates using Equations (3.15) through (3.17), one now proceeds using the same techniques that were introduced in Chapter 2. However, the addition of thermal effects does introduce certain difficulties with boundary conditions. These are discussed in the next section.

3.3. BOUNDARY CONDITIONS

Looking now at the boundary conditions associated with a thermoelastic plate, we can make comparisons with an isothermal plate, where again n denotes the direction normal to the edge and s the direction along the edge:

3.3.1. Simply Supported Edge

$$w = 0$$

$$M_n = 0 \tag{3.22}$$

In view of Equations (3.13) and (3.14), the latter equation above is in fact

$$M_n = 0 = -D\left[\frac{\partial^2 w}{\partial n^2} + \nu \frac{\partial^2 w}{\partial s^2} \right] - \frac{M^*}{1-\nu}$$

Since there is no curvature along the edge (i.e., $\partial^2 w/\partial s^2 = 0$), this equation becomes

$$\frac{\partial^2 w}{\partial n^2} = -\frac{M^*}{(1-\nu)D} \tag{3.23}$$

Hence the boundary conditions for a simply supported thermoelastic plate are nonhomogeneous.

3.3.2. Clamped Edge

$$w = 0 \tag{3.24}$$

$$\frac{\partial w}{\partial n} = 0 \tag{3.25}$$

These equations remain the same as those for the isothermal plate.

3.3.3. Free Edge

The boundary conditions are

$$M_n = 0 \quad \text{and} \quad V_n = 0$$

Hence, the first condition is given by Equation (3.23), and the second is seen from Equation (3.19) to be

$$\frac{\partial^3 w}{\partial n^3} + (2 - \nu) \frac{\partial^3 w}{\partial n \partial s^2} = - \frac{1}{D(1-\nu)} \frac{\partial M^*}{\partial n} \tag{3.26}$$

Here both boundary conditions are seen to be nonhomogeneous.

3.3.4. General

In many problems involving thermoelastic plates, it is seen that the boundary conditions are nonhomogeneous. Why is this important? In solving linear partial differential equations, separation of variables cannot be used with nonhomogeneous boundary conditions. Fortunately, methods are available to transform either homogeneous or nonhomogeneous partial differential equations with nonhomogeneous boundary conditions into nonhomogeneous partial differential equations with homogeneous boundary conditions, so that separation of variables may be used. A generalized method is presented in the next section.

3.4. GENERAL TREATMENT OF NONHOMOGENEOUS BOUNDARY CONDITIONS

Consider a plate with the $y = 0, b$ edges simply supported. The governing equation for the lateral deflection is Equation (3.15). From Equations (3.22) and (3.23) the boundary conditions are

$$w(x,0) = w(w,b) = 0 \tag{3.27}$$

$$\frac{\partial^2 w(x,0)}{\partial y^2} = - \frac{M^*(x,0)}{D(1-\nu)} = - \frac{M_1^*(x)}{D(1-\nu)} \tag{3.28}$$

$$\frac{\partial^2 w(x,b)}{\partial y^2} = - \frac{M^*(x,b)}{D(1-\nu)} = - \frac{M_2^*(x)}{D(1-\nu)} \tag{3.29}$$

where $M_1^*(x) \equiv M^*(x,0)$ and $M_2^* \equiv M^*(x,b)$.

We now introduce a function $\psi(x,y)$, which satisfies homogeneous boundary conditions on the $y=0$ and $y=b$ edges. Let

$$w(x,y) = \Psi(x,y) + f_1(y)M_1^*(x) + f_2(y)M_2^*(x) \qquad (3.30)$$

where for this problem we take $\Psi(x,y)$ to be of the Levy form:

$$\Psi(x,y) = \sum_{n=1}^{\infty} \phi_n(x) \sin \frac{n\pi y}{b} \qquad (3.31)$$

Also, in Equation (3.30) $f_1(y)$ and $f_2(y)$ are to be determined to satisfy the boundary conditions (3.27) through (3.29).

Substituting Equation (3.30) into Equations (3.27) through (3.29) results in

$$w(x,0) = \Psi(x,0) + f_1(0)M_1^*(x) + f_2(0)M_2^*(x) = 0$$

$$w(x,b) = \Psi(x,b) + f_1(b)M_1^*(x) + f_2(b)M_2^*(x) = 0$$

$$\frac{\partial^2 w(x,0)}{\partial y^2} = \frac{\partial^2 \Psi(x,0)}{\partial y^2} + f_1''(0)M_1^*(x) + f_2''(0)M_2^*(x) = -\frac{M_1^*(x)}{D(1-\nu)}$$

$$\frac{\partial^2 w(x,b)}{\partial y^2} = \frac{\partial^2 \Psi(x,b)}{\partial y^2} + f_1''(b)M_1^*(x) + f_2''(b)M_2^*(x) = -\frac{M_2^*(x)}{D(1-\nu)}$$

Since it was required that $\Psi(x,y)$ satisfy homogeneous boundary conditions at $y=0$ and $y=b$, it follows that

$$\Psi(x,0) = \Psi(x,b) = \frac{\partial^2 \Psi(x,0)}{\partial y^2} = \frac{\partial^2 \Psi(x,b)}{\partial y^2} = 0 \qquad (3.32)$$

Hence

$$f_1(0) = 0 \qquad\qquad f_2(0) = 0$$

$$f_1(b) = 0 \qquad\qquad f_2(b) = 0$$

$$f_1''(0) = -\frac{1}{D(1-\nu)} \qquad f_2''(0) = 0 \qquad\qquad (3.32a)$$

$$f_1''(b) = 0 \qquad\qquad f_2''(b) = -\frac{1}{D(1-\nu)}$$

54

Thermal Stresses in Plates

These are the only requirements on $f_1(y)$ and $f_2(y)$. Since there are four conditions on each function, each can be assumed to be a third-order polynomial.

Let

$$f_1(y) = c_0 + c_1 y + c_2 y^2 + c_3 y^3 \tag{3.33}$$

and

$$f_2(y) = k_0 + k_1 y + k_2 y^2 + k_3 y^3 \tag{3.34}$$

Substituting Equations (3.33) and (3.34) into (3.32a), we obtain

$$f_1(y) = \frac{1}{6bD(1-\nu)} (2b^2 y - 3by^2 + y^3) \tag{3.35}$$

$$f_2(y) = \frac{1}{6bD(1-\nu)} (b^2 y - y^3) \tag{3.36}$$

The use of Equations (3.35) and (3.36) and the substitution of Equation (3.30) into (3.15) results in the following:

$$D\nabla^4\Psi = p(x,y) - \frac{1}{1-\nu} \nabla^2 M^*$$

$$-\nabla^4\left\{ \frac{1}{6(1-\nu)b} (2b^2 y - 3by^2 + y^3) M_1^*(x) \right\} - \nabla^4\left\{ \frac{(b^2 y - y^3)}{6(1-\nu)b} M_2^*(x) \right\}$$

$$\tag{3.37}$$

Looking at Equation (3.37), it is seen that the original problem, which was Equation (3.15), with nonhomogeneous boundary conditions, Equations (3.27) through (3.29), has been transformed into a problem involving a "lateral deflection" Ψ, with homogeneous boundary conditions [Equation (3.32)] and an "altered loading," given by the right-hand side of Equation (3.37), which we now call $H(x,y)$. Hence

$$D\nabla^4\Psi = H(x,y) \tag{3.38}$$

Here $\Psi(x,y)$ is given by Equation (3.31), and $H(x,y)$ can be expanded correspondingly into a Fourier series as

$$H(x,y) = \sum_{n=1}^{\infty} h_n(x) \sin\lambda_n y \quad \text{where} \quad \lambda_n = \frac{n\pi}{b} \tag{3.39}$$

Substituting (3.31) and (3.39) into Equation (3.38) gives

$$D \sum_{n=1}^{\infty} \{ \phi_n^{IV} - 2\lambda_n^2 \phi_n'' + \lambda_n^4 \phi_n \} \sin\lambda_n y = \sum_{n=1}^{\infty} h_n(x) \sin\lambda_n y$$

Hence

$$\phi_n^{IV} - 2\lambda_n^2 \phi_n'' + \phi_n \lambda_n^4 = \frac{h_n(x)}{D} \tag{3.40}$$

It is seen that this has the same form of the ordinary differential equation in the Chapter 2 discussion of the Levy method. Now the boundary conditions at $x=0$ and $x=a$ can be considered. For a specific example, consider them to be simply supported also. Then

$$w(0,y) = w(a,y) = 0$$

$$M_x(0,y) = M_x(a,y) = 0 \quad \text{or} \quad \frac{\partial^2 w(0,y)}{\partial x^2} = -\frac{M^*(0,y)}{D(1-\nu)} \tag{3.41}$$

$$\frac{\partial^2 w(a,y)}{\partial x^2} = -\frac{M^*(a,y)}{D(1-\nu)}$$

Substituting Equation (3.30) into the above results in

$$w(0,y) = \Psi(0,y) + f_1(y)M_1^*(0) + f_2(y)M_2^*(0) = 0$$

$$w(a,y) = \Psi(a,y) + f_1(y)M_1^*(a) + f_2(y)M_2^*(a) = 0$$

$$\frac{\partial^2 w}{\partial x^2}(0,y) = \frac{\partial^2 \Psi}{\partial x^2}(0,y) + f_1(y)M_1^{*\prime\prime}(0) + f_2(y)M_2^{*\prime\prime}(a) = -\frac{M^*(0,y)}{D(1-\nu)}$$

$$\frac{\partial^2 w(a,y)}{\partial x^2} = \frac{\partial^2 \Psi(a,y)}{\partial x^2} + f_1(y)M_1^{*\prime\prime}(a) + f_2(y)M_2^{*\prime\prime}(a) = -\frac{M^*(a,y)}{D(1-\nu)}$$

Rearranging the above produces

$$\Psi(0,y) = -[f_1(y)M_1^*(0) + f_2(y)M_2^*(0)]$$

$$\Psi(a,y) = -[f_1(y)M_1^*(a) + f_2(y)M_2^*(a)]$$

$$\frac{\partial^2 \Psi(0,y)}{\partial x^2} = -\left[\frac{M^*(0,y)}{D(1-\nu)} + f_1(y)M_1^{*\prime\prime}(0) + f_2(y)M_2^{*\prime\prime}(0) \right] \tag{3.42}$$

$$\frac{\partial^2 \Psi(a,y)}{\partial x^2} = -\left[\frac{M^*(a,y)}{D(1-\nu)} + f_1(y)M_1^{*\prime\prime}(a) + f_2(y)M_2^{*\prime\prime}(a)\right]$$

Remembering that $\Psi(x,y)$ is given by Equation (3.31), it is logical to make the following expansions:

$$f_1(y) = \sum_{n=1}^{\infty} A_n \sin\lambda_n y \qquad M^*(0,y) = \sum_{n=1}^{\infty} C_n \sin\lambda_n y$$

$$f_2(y) = \sum_{n=1}^{\infty} B_n \sin\lambda_n y \qquad M^*(a,y) = \sum_{n=1}^{\infty} E_n \sin\lambda_n y \qquad (3.43)$$

Here A_n, B_n, C_n, and E_n are easily found. Substituting Equations (3.43) and (3.31) into Equation (3.42) and equating all coefficients results in

$$\phi_n(0) = -\left[A_n M_1^*(0) + B_n M_2^*(0)\right]$$

$$\phi_n(a) = -\left[A_n M_1^*(a) + B_n M_2^*(a)\right]$$

$$\phi_n''(0) = -\left[\frac{C_n}{D(1-\nu)} + A_n M_1^{*\prime\prime}(0) + B_n M_2^{*\prime\prime}(0)\right] \qquad (3.44)$$

$$\phi_n''(a) = -\left[\frac{E_n}{D(1-\nu)} + A_n M_1^{*\prime\prime}(a) + B_n M_2^{*\prime\prime}(a)\right]$$

Hence these four boundary values provide the necessary information to determine the constants in the solution of Equation (3.40), which is

$$\phi_n(x) = (K_1 + K_2 x)\cosh\lambda_n x + (K_3 + K_4 x)\sinh\lambda_n x + \eta_n(x) \quad (3.45)$$

Here $\eta_n(x)$ is the particular solution. Using this, then, Equation (3.31) is completely solved, and in turn Equation (3.30) is solved.

This general approach can be used to solve any plate problem involving nonhomogeneous boundary conditions.

3.5. REFERENCES

There are two references that are particularly good concerning thermal stresses in plates, as well as in other structural elements in general, including shells, rings, beams, etc. They are:

1. Bruno A Boley and Jerome H. Weiner, *Theory of Thermal Stresses*, Wiley, 1962.
2. D. J. Johns, *Thermal Stress Analyses*, Pergamon, 1965.

3.6. PROBLEMS

3.1. A flat structural panel on the wing of a supersonic fighter is considered to be unstressed at 70°F. After a time at cruise speed such that
   a steady-state temperature distribution is reached, the temperature
   on the heated side is measured at 140°F, the temperature on the
   cooler side is measured at 80°F, and the temperature gradient
   through the plate is considered to be constant. (See Sketch 3.2.)
   Calculate the thermal stress resultant N^* and the thermal stress
   couple M^*, where for aluminum $E = 10 \times 10^6$ psi $\gamma = 10 \times 10^{-6}$ in.
   /(in.)(°F), and $\nu = 0.3$.

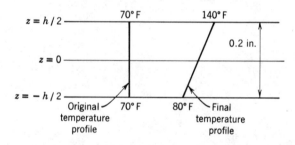

Sketch 3.2

3.2. The same aluminum panel as in Problem 1 is now heated symmetri-
   cally from both the top side and the bottom side. After 10 sec
   thermocouples placed on both surfaces of the panel read 160°F, and
   a thermocouple at the midsurface reads 80°F. Assuming the temperature profile in the panel to be parabolic (i.e., a second-degree
   polynomial), what is the thermal stress resultant N^* and the thermal
   stress couple M^* at this time?

3.3. In Problem 3.1, at what location across the plate thickness are σ_x and
   σ_y at a maximum, and what is that stress, if one assumes that
   $N_x = N_y = M_x = M_y = 0$?

3.4. In Problem 3.2, at what location across the plate thickness do σ_x and σ_y have their maximum value and what is the value, if one assumes that $N_x = N_y = M_x = M_y = 0$?

3.5. Another aluminum panel 0.4 in. thick, and stress-free at 70°F is subjected to transient heating on one of its surfaces such that $T = T(z)$ only, as in the previous problems. Thermocouples record at a critical time that $T(h/2) = 170°F$, $T(0) = 130°F$, and $T(-h/2) = 100°F$. Assuming a polynomial temperature distribution, calculate N^*, M^*, and $\sigma_{x\,max} = \sigma_{y\,max}$, assuming N_x, N_y, M_x, and $M_y = 0$.

4

CIRCULAR PLATES

4.1. INTRODUCTION

In the three previous chapters, all consideration has been of rectangular plates. Primarily, this is because we all are used to Cartesian reference frames—we can visualize the equilibrium of forces and moments, as well as elasticity relationships, more easily in an x-y-z coordinate frame.

However, circular-plate structural elements are encountered in all phases of engineering. It is therefore necessary to develop an understanding of the behavior of circular plates.

Consider the following element from a circular plate, with positive directions of stresses and deflections shown in Fig. 4.1:

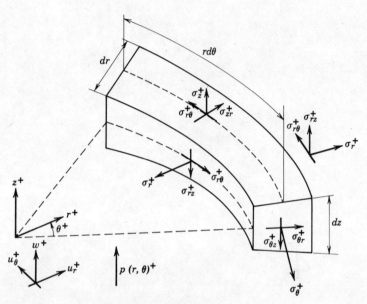

Fig. 4.1.   Circular plate element.

4.2.   GOVERNING EQUATIONS

The equations of elasticity can be derived directly in a circular cylindrical coordinate system, or can be obtained by transforming the elasticity equations given in Chapter 1 through the use of the relationships

$$x = r\cos\theta, \quad y = r\sin\theta, \quad \text{and} \quad x^2 + y^2 = r^2$$

However, they are merely presented here in their final form.

4.2.1.   Equilibrium Equations in Circular Cylindrical Coordinates

$$\frac{\partial \sigma_r}{\partial r} + \frac{1}{r}\frac{\partial \sigma_{r\theta}}{\partial \theta} + \frac{\partial \sigma_{rz}}{\partial z} + \frac{\sigma_r - \sigma_\theta}{r} = 0 \tag{4.1}$$

$$\frac{\partial \sigma_{r\theta}}{\partial r} + \frac{1}{r}\frac{\partial \sigma_\theta}{\partial \theta} + \frac{\partial \sigma_{\theta z}}{\partial z} + \frac{2}{r}\sigma_{r\theta} = 0 \tag{4.2}$$

$$\frac{\partial \sigma_{rz}}{\partial r} + \frac{1}{r}\frac{\partial \sigma_{\theta z}}{\partial \theta} + \frac{\partial \sigma_z}{\partial z} + \frac{1}{r}\sigma_{rz} = 0 \tag{4.3}$$

4.2.2. Stress-Strain Relations
(After Using Plate Assumptions)

$$\varepsilon_r = \frac{1}{E}[\sigma_r - \nu\sigma_\theta] \tag{4.4}$$

$$\varepsilon_\theta = \frac{1}{E}[\sigma_\theta - \nu\sigma_r] \tag{4.5}$$

$$\varepsilon_{r\theta} = \frac{1}{2G}\sigma_{r\theta} \tag{4.6}$$

$$\sigma_z = \varepsilon_{rz} = \varepsilon_{\theta z} = 0 \tag{4.7}$$

4.2.3. Strain-Displacement Relations, General

$$\varepsilon_r = \frac{\partial u_r}{\partial r}; \qquad \varepsilon_\theta = \frac{1}{r}\frac{\partial u_\theta}{\partial \theta} + \frac{u_r}{r}; \qquad \varepsilon_z = \frac{\partial w}{\partial z} \tag{4.8, 9, 10}$$

$$\varepsilon_{r\theta} = \frac{1}{2}\left(\frac{1}{r}\frac{\partial u_r}{\partial \theta} + \frac{\partial u_\theta}{\partial r} - \frac{u_\theta}{r}\right) \tag{4.11}$$

$$\varepsilon_{\theta z} = \frac{1}{2}\left(\frac{\partial u_\theta}{\partial z} + \frac{1}{r}\frac{\partial w}{\partial \theta}\right) \tag{4.12}$$

$$\varepsilon_{rz} = \frac{1}{2}\left(\frac{\partial w}{\partial r} + \frac{\partial u_r}{\partial z}\right) \tag{4.13}$$

Of course, for a classical plate $\varepsilon_z = \varepsilon_{rz} = \varepsilon_{\theta z} = 0$ in Equations (4.10), (4.12), and (4.13) above.

As in the case of rectangular plates, the stress resultants, stress couples, and shear resultants are defined as follows:

$$\left\{\begin{matrix} N_r \\ N_\theta \\ N_{r\theta} \end{matrix}\right\} = \int_{-h/2}^{h/2} \left\{\begin{matrix} \sigma_r \\ \sigma_\theta \\ \sigma_{r\theta} \end{matrix}\right\} dz \tag{4.14}$$

$$\begin{Bmatrix} M_r \\ M_\theta \\ M_{r\theta} \end{Bmatrix} = \int_{-h/2}^{h/2} \begin{Bmatrix} \sigma_r \\ \sigma_\theta \\ \sigma_{r\theta} \end{Bmatrix} z \, dz \tag{4.15}$$

$$\begin{Bmatrix} Q_r \\ Q_\theta \end{Bmatrix} = \int_{-h/2}^{h/2} \begin{Bmatrix} \sigma_{rz} \\ \sigma_{\theta z} \end{Bmatrix} dz \tag{4.16}$$

In developing the governing equations for a circular plate, one proceeds as in Chapter 1, multiplying Equations (4.1) through (4.3) by dz and integrating the equations across the thickness of the plate, then multiplying (4.1) and (4.2) by $z \, dz$ and again integrating across the plate thickness. The results are

$$\frac{\partial N_r}{\partial r} + \frac{1}{r} \frac{\partial N_{r\theta}}{\partial \theta} + \frac{N_r - N_\theta}{r} = 0 \tag{4.17}$$

$$\frac{\partial N_{r\theta}}{\partial r} + \frac{1}{r} \frac{\partial N_\theta}{\partial \theta} + \frac{2}{r} N_{r\theta} = 0 \tag{4.18}$$

$$\frac{\partial Q_r}{\partial r} + \frac{1}{r} \frac{\partial Q_\theta}{\partial \theta} + \frac{1}{r} Q_r + p(r,\theta) = 0 \tag{4.19}$$

$$\frac{\partial M_r}{\partial r} + \frac{1}{r} \frac{\partial M_{r\theta}}{\partial \theta} + \frac{M_r - M_\theta}{r} - Q_r = 0 \tag{4.20}$$

$$\frac{\partial M_{r\theta}}{\partial r} + \frac{1}{r} \frac{\partial M_\theta}{\partial \theta} + \frac{2}{r} M_{r\theta} - Q_\theta = 0 \tag{4.21}$$

As in Chapter 1, for the bending of a circular plate the displacements are written in the form

$$u_r = u_{0r} + \alpha z, \quad u_\theta = u_{0\theta} + \beta z, \quad \text{and} \quad w = w(r,\theta) \tag{4.22}$$

Since in a classical circular plate $\varepsilon_{rz} = \varepsilon_{\theta z} = 0$, substituting Equation (4.22) into Equations (4.12) and (4.13) results in

$$\alpha = -\frac{\partial w}{\partial r} \quad \text{and} \quad \beta = -\frac{1}{r} \frac{\partial w}{\partial \theta} \quad \text{or}$$

$$u_r = u_{0r} - z \frac{\partial w}{\partial r}, \quad u_\theta = u_{0\theta} - \frac{z}{r} \frac{\partial w}{\partial \theta} \tag{4.23}$$

From Equations (4.23), (4.8), and (4.4),

$$\varepsilon_r = \frac{\partial u_r}{\partial r} = \frac{1}{E}[\sigma_r - \nu\sigma_\theta] = \frac{\partial u_{0r}}{\partial r} - z\frac{\partial^2 w}{\partial r^2} \qquad (4.24)$$

From Equations (4.23), (4.9), and (4.5),

$$\varepsilon_\theta = \frac{1}{r}\frac{\partial u_\theta}{\partial \theta} + \frac{u_r}{r} = \frac{1}{E}[\sigma_\theta - \nu\sigma_r] = \frac{1}{r}\frac{\partial u_{0\theta}}{\partial \theta} + \frac{u_{0r}}{r} - \frac{z}{r^2}\frac{\partial^2 w}{\partial \theta^2} - \frac{z}{r}\frac{\partial w}{\partial r} \qquad (4.25)$$

From Equations (4.23), (4.11), and (4.6),

$$\varepsilon_{r\theta} = \frac{1}{2G}\sigma_{r\theta} = \frac{1+\nu}{E}\sigma_{r\theta} = \frac{1}{2}\left(\frac{1}{r}\frac{\partial u_{0r}}{\partial \theta} + \frac{\partial u_{0\theta}}{\partial r} - \frac{u_{0\theta}}{r}\right)$$

$$- \frac{2z}{r}\frac{\partial^2 w}{\partial r\partial \theta} + \frac{2z}{r^2}\frac{\partial w}{\partial \theta} \qquad (4.26)$$

Multiplying Equations (4.24) through (4.26) by dz, integrate across the thickness of the plate; then multiply them by $z\,dz$ and again integrate them across the plate thickness. With some algebraic manipulation, the stress-resultant–in-plane-displacement relations and moment-curvature relations for a circular plate (in the case where there are no surface shear stresses) may then be derived:

$$N_r = K\left[\frac{\partial u_{0r}}{\partial r} + \frac{\nu}{r}\frac{\partial u_{0\theta}}{\partial \theta} + \nu\frac{u_{0r}}{r}\right] \qquad (4.27)$$

$$N_\theta = K\left[\frac{1}{r}\frac{\partial u_{0\theta}}{\partial \theta} + \frac{u_{0r}}{r} + \nu\frac{\partial u_{0r}}{\partial r}\right] \qquad (4.28)$$

$$N_{r\theta} = K(1-\nu)\left[\frac{1}{r}\frac{\partial u_{0r}}{\partial \theta} + \frac{\partial u_{0\theta}}{\partial r} - \frac{u_{0\theta}}{r}\right] \qquad (4.29)$$

$$M_r = -D\left[\frac{\partial^2 w}{\partial r^2} + \frac{\nu}{r}\frac{\partial w}{\partial r} + \frac{\nu}{r^2}\frac{\partial^2 w}{\partial \theta^2}\right] \qquad (4.30)$$

$$M_\theta = -D\left[\frac{1}{r^2}\frac{\partial^2 w}{\partial \theta^2} + \frac{1}{r}\frac{\partial w}{\partial r} + \nu\frac{\partial^2 w}{\partial r^2}\right] \qquad (4.31)$$

$$M_{r\theta} = -D(1-\nu)\left[\frac{1}{r}\frac{\partial^2 w}{\partial r \partial \theta} - \frac{1}{r^2}\frac{\partial w}{\partial \theta}\right] \tag{4.32}$$

where again $K = Eh/(1-\nu^2)$ and $D = Eh^3/12(1-\nu^2)$.

Solving Equations (4.20) and (4.21) for Q_r and Q_θ, and substituting the results into Equation (4.19), we obtain an equation involving M_r, M_θ, $M_{r\theta}$, and $p(r,\theta)$. Substituting Equations (4.25) through (4.27) into that equation results in the final governing differential equation for the bending of a circular plate:

$$D\nabla^4 w = p(r,\theta) \tag{4.33}$$

where $\quad \nabla^2(\ ) = \dfrac{\partial^2(\ )}{\partial r^2} + \dfrac{1}{r}\dfrac{\partial(\ )}{\partial r} + \dfrac{1}{r^2}\dfrac{\partial^2(\ )}{\partial \theta^2} \tag{4.34}$

Similarly, substituting Equations (4.27) through (4.29) into Equations (4.17) and (4.18) produces the equations for the stretching of a circular plate:

$$\left.\begin{array}{c} \nabla^4 u_{0r} = 0 \\[4pt] \nabla^4 u_{0\theta} = 0 \end{array}\right\} \tag{4.35}$$

Of course, once the plate solution is obtained, the stresses within the plate are given by

$$\sigma_r = \frac{N_r}{h} + \frac{M_r z}{h^3/12}$$

$$\sigma_\theta = \frac{N_\theta}{h} + \frac{M_\theta z}{h^3/12}$$

$$\sigma_{r\theta} = \frac{N_{r\theta}}{h} + \frac{M_{r\theta} z}{h^3/12} \tag{4.36}$$

$$\sigma_{rz} = \frac{3Q_r}{2h}\left[1 - \left(\frac{z}{h/2}\right)^2\right]$$

$$\sigma_{\theta z} = \frac{3Q_\theta}{2h}\left[1 - \left(\frac{z}{h/2}\right)^2\right]$$

For the case of surface shear stresses the last two expressions above are replaced by the analogous expressions of Chapter 1, simply modified by changing the subscripts x and y to r and θ.

Furthermore, to consider a thermoelastic circular plate, one merely adds terms to Equations (4.27), (4.28), (4.30), (4.31), (4.33), (4.35), and the first two of (4.36), analogous to the thermal terms appearing in Equations (3.11), (3.12), (3.13), (3.14), (3.15), (3.16), (3.17), and (3.20).

In the general case where axial symmetry is absent, the solution of Equation (4.28) results in Bessel functions and modified Bessel functions of the first and second kinds. Such problems are not treated here.

4.3. AXIALLY SYMMETRIC CIRCULAR PLATES

When the plate is continuous in the θ direction (i.e., is in the region $0 \leqslant \theta \leqslant 2\pi$), when the loading is not a function of θ, and when the boundary conditions do not vary around the circumference, the plate problem is said to be axially symmetric, and the following simplifications can be made:

$$\frac{\partial(\ )}{\partial \theta} = \frac{\partial^2(\ )}{\partial \theta^2} = M_{r\theta} = Q_\theta = 0$$

The previous equations for the bending of a circular plate can therefore be simplified to the following, where primes denote differentiation with respect to r:

$$M_r = -D\left(w'' + \frac{\nu}{r}w'\right) \tag{4.37}$$

$$M_\theta = -D\left(\frac{1}{r}w' + \nu w''\right) \tag{4.38}$$

$$Q_r = -D(\nabla^2 w)' \tag{4.39}$$

$$D\nabla^4 w = p(r) \tag{4.40}$$

where $\quad \nabla^2 = (\ )'' + \frac{1}{r}(\ )' = \frac{1}{r}\frac{d}{dr}\left[r\frac{d(\ )}{dr}\right]$

Interestingly, Equation (4.40) can therefore be written as,

$$\nabla^4 w = \frac{1}{r}\frac{d}{dr}\left\{r\frac{d}{dr}\left[\frac{1}{r}\frac{d}{dr}\left(r\frac{dw}{dr}\right)\right]\right\} = \frac{p(r)}{D} \qquad (4.41)$$

4.4. SOLUTIONS FOR AXIALLY SYMMETRIC CIRCULAR PLATES

Equation (4.41) can be made dimensionless by normalizing both the radial coordinate r and the lateral deflection w with respect to the radius of the circular plate, a, as follows:

$$\bar{r} = \frac{r}{a}, \qquad \bar{w} = \frac{w}{a} \qquad (4.42)$$

Using Equation (4.42) above, Equation (4.41) can be written as

$$\frac{1}{\bar{r}}\frac{d}{d\bar{r}}\left\{\bar{r}\frac{d}{d\bar{r}}\left[\frac{1}{\bar{r}}\frac{d}{d\bar{r}}\left(\bar{r}\frac{d\bar{w}}{d\bar{r}}\right)\right]\right\} = p(\bar{r})\frac{a^3}{D}. \qquad (4.43)$$

One can proceed to obtain the homogeneous solution of Equation (4.43) above, by setting the right-hand side equal to zero and integrating the left-hand side. This is done in detail below; C_0, C_1, C_2, and C_3 are the resulting constants of integration, used to satisfy boundary conditions.

Multiplying the homogeneous portion of Equation (4.43) by $\bar{r}$ and then integrating once yields

$$\frac{d}{d\bar{r}}\left[\frac{1}{\bar{r}}\frac{d}{d\bar{r}}\left(\bar{r}\frac{d\bar{w}}{d\bar{r}}\right)\right] = \frac{C_0}{\bar{r}}$$

Integrating once and multiplying both sides by $\bar{r}$ then provides

$$\frac{d}{d\bar{r}}\left(\bar{r}\frac{d\bar{w}}{d\bar{r}}\right) = C_0\bar{r}\ln\bar{r} + C_1\bar{r}$$

To integrate the first term on the right-hand side let $\ln\bar{r}\equiv y$, hence $\bar{r}=e^y$, and $d\bar{r}=e^y\,dy$. Then

$$\int \bar{r}\ln\bar{r}\,d\bar{r} = \int ye^{2y}\,dy = \frac{ye^{2y}}{2} - \frac{e^{2y}}{4}$$

Therefore, integrating the expression above and dividing the results by $\bar{r}$ gives

$$\frac{d\bar{w}}{d\bar{r}} = C_0\left[\frac{\bar{r}\ln\bar{r}}{2} - \frac{\bar{r}}{4}\right] + \frac{C_1\bar{r}}{2} + \frac{C_2}{\bar{r}},$$

and finally, after more integration,

$$\bar{w} = \frac{C_0}{2}\left[\frac{\bar{r}^2\ln\bar{r}}{2} - \frac{\bar{r}^2}{4}\right] - \frac{C_0\bar{r}^2}{8} + \frac{C_1\bar{r}^2}{4} + C_2\ln\bar{r} + C_3$$

This final form of the homogeneous solution can be written more succinctly as

$$\bar{w} = A + B\ln\bar{r} + C\bar{r}^2 + E\bar{r}^2\ln\bar{r} \qquad (4.44)$$

Returning to Equation (4.43), we can write the particular solution as

$$\bar{w}_p = \int\frac{1}{\bar{r}}\int\bar{r}\int\frac{1}{\bar{r}}\int\frac{p(\bar{r})a^3}{D}\bar{r}\,d\bar{r}\,d\bar{r}\,d\bar{r}\,d\bar{r} \qquad (4.45)$$

Thus the total solution for any circular plate under axially symmetric loading is given by Equations (4.44) and (4.45). It is easy to show that the particular solution for a plate with a uniform lateral load is

$$\bar{w}_p = \frac{p_0 a^3\bar{r}^4}{64D} \quad\text{or}\quad w_p = \frac{p_0 r^4}{64D} \qquad (4.46)$$

For ease of calculation, the following quantities are given explicitly for the circular plate of radius a with uniform lateral loading $p(r)=p_0$:

$$\bar{w} = A + B\ln\bar{r} + C\bar{r}^2 + E\bar{r}^2\ln\bar{r} + \frac{p_0 a^3\bar{r}^4}{64D} \qquad (4.47)$$

$$\frac{d\bar{w}}{d\bar{r}} = \frac{B}{\bar{r}} + 2C\bar{r} + E[2\bar{r}\ln\bar{r} + \bar{r}] + \frac{p_0 a^3\bar{r}^3}{16D} \qquad (4.48)$$

$$M_r = -\frac{D}{a}\left[-\frac{B}{\bar{r}^2}(1-\nu) + 2C(1+\nu) + 2E(1+\nu)\ln\bar{r} + (3+\nu)E \right]$$

$$-\frac{p_0 a^2 \bar{r}^2 (3+\nu)}{16} \tag{4.49}$$

$$Q_r = -\frac{D}{a^2}\left[\frac{4E}{\bar{r}} \right] - \frac{p_0 a \bar{r}}{2} \tag{4.50}$$

$$M_\theta = -\frac{D}{a}\left[\frac{B(1-\nu)}{\bar{r}^2} + 2C(1+\nu) + 2E\ln\bar{r}(1+\nu) + E(1+3\nu) \right]$$

$$-\frac{p_0 a^2 \bar{r}^2 (1+3\nu)}{16} \tag{4.51}$$

If the lateral loading were different, only the last terms in each expression above would be changed; the homogeneous solution would remain the same.

4.5. CIRCULAR PLATE, SIMPLY SUPPORTED AT THE OUTER EDGE, SUBJECTED TO UNIFORM LATERAL LOADING p_0

For a plate that is continuous from $0 \leqslant r \leqslant a$, and that bears no concentrated load at $r = 0$, it is easy to see that $B = E = 0$; otherwise the lateral deflection and transverse shear resultant would be infinite at $\bar{r} = 0$. At $\bar{r} = 1$ or $r = a$, the boundary conditions are

$$\bar{w}(1) = 0$$

$$M_r(1) = 0$$

Hence $A = \frac{5+\nu}{1+\nu}\frac{p_0 a^3}{64D}$, $C = -\frac{p_0 a^3 (3+\nu)}{32D(1+\nu)}$

and

$$w(\bar{r}) = \frac{p_0 a^4}{64D}\left[\frac{5+\nu}{1+\nu} - \frac{2(3+\nu)\bar{r}^2}{1+\nu} + \bar{r}^4 \right] \tag{4.52}$$

4.6. CIRCULAR PLATE, CLAMPED AT THE OUTER EDGE, SUBJECTED TO UNIFORM LATERAL LOADING p_0

Again $B=E=0$. At the outer edge $\bar{w}(1)=0$ and $d\bar{w}(1)/d\bar{r}=0$. Hence $A=p_0a^3/64D$ and $C=-p_0a^3/32D$. Thus

$$w(\bar{r}) = \frac{p_0a^4}{64D}[1-2\bar{r}^2+\bar{r}^4] \qquad (4.53)$$

4.7. ANNULAR PLATE, SIMPLY SUPPORTED AT THE OUTER EDGE, SUBJECTED TO A STRESS COUPLE M, AT THE INNER BOUNDARY

The configuration is shown in Sketch 4.1. Remembering that $\bar{r}=r/a$, we define $s=b/a$. The governing differential equation in this case, with no lateral load $p(r)$, is

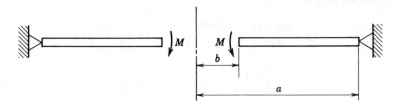

Sketch 4.1

$$\nabla^4 w = 0,$$

and the boundary conditions are

$$\bar{w}(1)=0 \qquad M_r(s)=M$$

$$M_r(1)=0 \qquad Q_r(s)=0$$

The lateral deflection is found to be

$$w(\bar{r}) = \frac{Ma^2s^2\ln\bar{r}}{D(1-\nu)(1-s^2)} - \frac{Ma^2}{2D(1+\nu)}\left(\frac{s^2}{1-s^2}\right)(1-\bar{r}^2) \qquad (4.54)$$

4.8. ANNULAR PLATE, SIMPLY SUPPORTED AT THE OUTER EDGE, SUBJECTED TO A SHEAR RESULTANT Q_0 AT THE INNER BOUNDARY

For the situation in Sketch 4.2, again, the governing differential equation is $\nabla^4 w = 0$, and the boundary conditions are

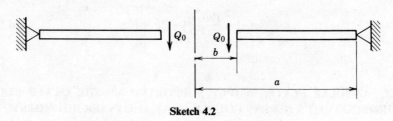

Sketch 4.2

$$\bar{w}(1) = 0 \qquad M_r(s) = 0$$

$$M_r(1) = 0 \qquad Q_r(s) = Q_0$$

The solution is

$$w(\bar{r}) = \frac{Q_0 s a^3}{4D}\left[-\frac{(3+\nu)(1-\bar{r}^2)}{2(1+\nu)} + \frac{s^2 \ln s}{(1-s^2)}(1-\bar{r}^2) \right.$$

$$\left. -2\frac{1+\nu}{1-\nu}\frac{s^2}{1-s^2}\ln s \ln \bar{r} - \bar{r}^2 \ln \bar{r} \right] \qquad (4.55)$$

4.9. GENERAL REMARKS

Of course the solutions given in Sections 4.5 through 4.8 can be superimposed to form the solutions to other problems. Suppose one had an annular plate, simply supported at its outer edge, subjected to a stress couple M as well as a transverse shear resultant Q_0, acting on the inner boundary, as shown in Sketch 4.3 below,

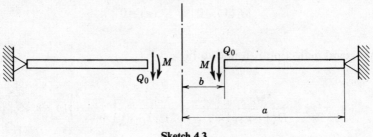

Sketch 4.3

The solution is the sum of Equations (4.54) and (4.55). All other stress quantities are found by substituting this sum into Equations (4.36) through (4.38).

As another example using the previous examples as building blocks, consider the problem shown in Sketch 4.4 below: This simply supported circular plate is subjected to a ring load of R (lb/in. of circumference). To solve this problem one first divides the plate problem into two parts: an inner solution 1 extending over the region $0 \leqslant r \leqslant b$, and an outer solution 2 over the region $b \leqslant r \leqslant a$. In each case the governing equation is

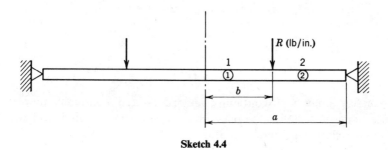

Sketch 4.4

$$\nabla^4 w_1 = 0 \quad \text{and} \quad \nabla^4 w_2 = 0$$

and eight boundary conditions are needed. Since there is no lateral load $p(r)$, the solution to each equation, with suitable subscript, is Equation (4.47) with $p_0 = 0$ (i.e., the homogeneous solution. From the reasoning of Sections 4.5 and 4.6, it is seen that $B_1 = E_1 = 0$. Likewise from the reasoning of Sections 4.5, 4.7, and 4.8, at $r = a$ or $\bar{r} = 1$, $\bar{w}_2(1) = M_{r2}(1) = 0$.

At the junction of the two plate segments, it is obvious that the lateral deflection, the slopes, and the stress couples must be equal for both; hence

$$w_1(b) = w_2(b) \quad \text{or} \quad \bar{w}_1(s) = \bar{w}_2(s)$$

$$\frac{dw_1(b)}{dr} = \frac{dw_2(b)}{dr} \quad \text{or} \quad \frac{d\bar{w}_1(s)}{d\bar{r}} = \frac{d\bar{w}_2(s)}{d\bar{r}}$$

$$M_{r1}(b) = M_{r2}(b) \quad \text{or} \quad M_{r1}(s) = M_{r2}(s)$$

The eighth and last boundary condition is obtained by looking closely at the shear condition at $r=b$, as seen in Sketch 4.5 below: The boundary condition is $R=Q_2(b)-Q_1(b)$.

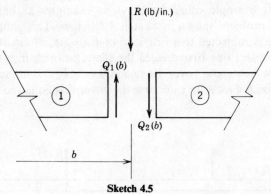

Sketch 4.5

If one has either a discontinuity in load or a discontinuity in plate thickness, one must divide the plate into two segments. Examples of such problems are shown in Sketch 4.6 below.

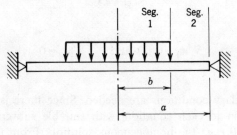

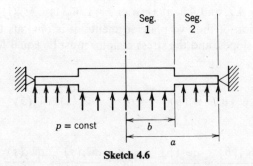

Sketch 4.6

It should be noted that in the example on the left the lateral load over segment 1 is a negative number, whereas in the example on the right it is a positive number, since $p(r)$ is positive in the positive direction of the lateral deflection w. Further it should be noted that in each of these examples, because there is no concentrated ring load R as in the previous example, the eighth boundary condition is $Q_1(b) = Q_2(b)$.

Of course if one has n structural and/or loading discontinuities, one then must use $n+1$ segments and $4(n+1)$ boundary conditions.

Use of Equations (4.47) through (4.51), with the proper last terms (the particular solution) obtained by solving Equation (4.45), reduces the solution of these problems to a straightforward procedure. Subsequently, the stresses are found through Equation (4.36).

4.10. PROBLEMS

4.1. The circular flooring in a silo of radius a is solidly supported at the walls in such a way that the floor plate may be considered to be clamped. If grain is poured onto the floor so that the floor loading is triangular in cross section, as shown in Sketch 4.7 below, what is the expression for the deflection at the center of the floor?

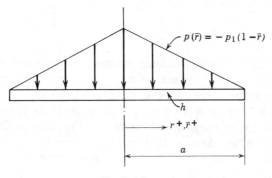

$$p(\bar{r}) = -p_1(1 - \bar{r})$$

Sketch 4.7

4.2. Consider a circular plate of radius a, shown in Sketch 4.8 below, loaded by an edge couple $M_r = M$ at the outer edge. Find the value of the stress couples M_r and M_θ throughout the plate.

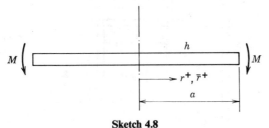

Sketch 4.8

4.3.   The flat head of a piston in an internal-combustion engine is consi-
       dered to be a plate of radius a, where the center support to the
       connecting rod is of radius b, as shown in Sketch 4.9. If the
       maximum down pressure is uniform with magnitude $p(r) = -p_0$,
       determine the location and magnitude of the maximum bending
       stress. Assume that the head is clamped on both edges.

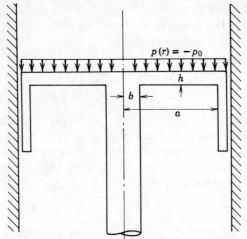

Sketch 4.9

4.4.   A certain pressure tranducer operates by the pressure in a chamber
       deflecting a thin circular plate. A rigid member joined to it at the
       center is thus deflected and, through a linkage mechanism (shown in
       Sketch 4.10) deflects a pointer on a gauge to the right. Determine the
       expression relating the deflection δ of the gauge to the pressure p_0 in
       the chamber. Assume that neither the rigid piece nor the linkages
       affect the deflection of the plate. Also assume that the circular plate
       is simply supported.

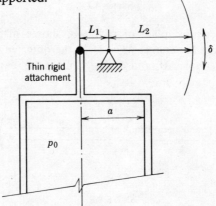

Sketch 4.10

4.5. An underwater instrumentation canister is a cylinder with ends that are circular plates that can be considered clamped at the outer edges, $r = a$ or $\bar{r} = 1$ as shown in Sketch 4.11. In order to design the ends (i.e., choose the thickness h) for a given material, one must determine the location and magnitude of the maximum stress when the canister is under water at ambient pressure p_0. Assume that the cylindrical portion introduces no in-plane loads on the ends. Find the maximum radial stress. Also, what is the maximum circumferential stress? What elastic properties of the material are involved in finding the maximum radial stress? The maximum circumferential stress?

Sketch 4.11

4.6. A flat circular plate roof is being designed to fit over an unused cave entrance. The outer radius is a, the thickness is h, and the outer edge is considered clamped. If the weight density of the material used is ρ (lb/in.^{3}), what are the maximum deflection and the maximum stress in the plate due to gravity alone?

4.7. An air pump is constructed out of a shaft, to which is clamped a disk of uniform thickness, at whose outer edge a soft gasket prevents air passage between the disk and the surrounding cylinder, as shown in Sketch 4.12 .

   Assuming that the disk is clamped to the shaft of radius b, and free at its outer edge of radius a, and that a maximum differential pressure of p_0 (psi) can be built up, what is the maximum radial stress? What is the maximum shear resultant, Q_r (lb/in.)? Could Q_r have been determined in another way?

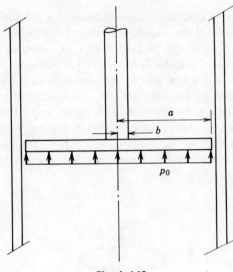

Sketch 4.12

4.8. In a chemical plant, a certain process involving high gaseous pressures requires a blowout diaphragm that will blow at 100-psi pressure in order that expensive equipment will not be damaged. The flat diaphragm is 10 in. in radius, simply supported on its outer edge. It is made of a brittle material with $\nu = \frac{1}{3}$ and an ultimate tensile strength of 50,000 psi. What thickness is required to have the plate fracture when the lateral pressure reaches 100 psi?

5

BUCKLING OF THIN PLATES

5.1. DERIVATION OF THE GOVERNING EQUATIONS

We have previously derived the governing equations for a thin plate
subjected to both lateral and in-plane loads. Among those equations there
was one describing the relationship between the lateral deflection and the
laterally distributed loading,

$$D\nabla^4 w = p(x,y), \tag{5.1}$$

as well as equations dealing with in-plane displacements (related to in-plane loads),

$$\nabla^4 u_0 = \nabla^4 v_0 = 0 \tag{5.2}$$

As discussed previously, the equation involving lateral displacements and loads is completely independent of (uncoupled from) those involving the in-plane displacements and loads.

However, it is found that if the in-plane loads are compressive, then upon attaining certain discrete values, they do result in lateral displacements. Thus there does occur a coupling between in-plane loads and lateral displacements, w. As a result, a more inclusive theory must be developed to account for this phenomenon, which is called buckling or elastic instability.

You have noted this phenomenon previously in your course on the mechanics of materials, in the study of the buckling of columns.

In contrast with the development of the governing plate equations in Chapter 1, which began with the three-dimensional equations of elasticity, we here begin by looking at the in-plane forces acting on a plate element, in which the forces are assumed to be functions of the midsurface coordinates x and y, as shown in Figure 5.1 below.

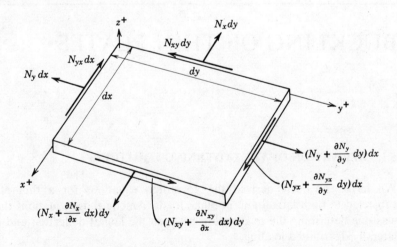

Fig. 5.1. In-plane forces on a plate element.

In Sketch 5.1 below, such a plate element is viewed from the midsurface in the positive y direction. The relationship between forces and displacements is shown when the plate is subjected to both lateral and in-plane forces, so that there is a lateral deflection w. (Obviously, the deflection is exaggerated.)

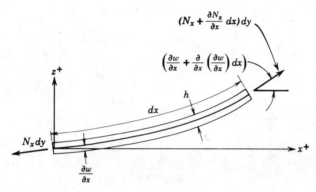

Sketch 5.1

Hence the z component of the N_x loading per unit area is, for small slopes (i.e., such that the sine of the angle equals the angle itself in radians),

$$\frac{1}{dx\,dy}\left[\left(N_x+\frac{\partial N_x}{\partial x}\,dx\right)dy\left(\frac{\partial w}{\partial x}+\frac{\partial^2 w}{\partial x^2}\,dx\right)-N_x\,dy\,\frac{\partial w}{\partial x}\right]$$

Neglecting terms of higher order, the force per unit planform area in the z direction is seen to be

$$N_x\frac{\partial^2 w}{\partial x^2}+\frac{\partial N_x}{\partial x}\,\frac{\partial w}{\partial x}$$

Similarly, the z component of the N_y force per unit planform area is

$$N_y\frac{\partial^2 w}{\partial y^2}+\frac{\partial N_y}{\partial y}\,\frac{\partial w}{\partial y}$$

Finally, to investigate the z component of the in-plane shear resultants N_{xy} and N_{yx}, we use Sketch 5.2: Here the z component per unit area of the in-plane shear resultants is

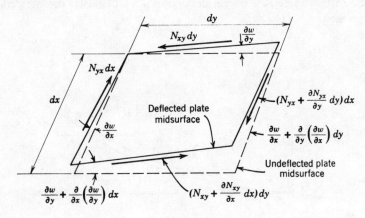

Sketch 5.2

$$\frac{1}{dx\,dy}\left\{\left(N_{xy}+\frac{\partial N_{xy}}{\partial x}dx\right)\left(\frac{\partial w}{\partial y}+\frac{\partial^2 w}{\partial x\partial y}dx\right)dy\right.$$

$$\left.+\left(N_{yx}+\frac{\partial N_{yx}}{\partial y}dy\right)\left(\frac{\partial w}{\partial x}+\frac{\partial^2 w}{\partial x\partial y}dy\right)dx-N_{xy}\frac{\partial w}{\partial y}dy-N_{yx}\frac{\partial w}{\partial x}dx\right\}$$

If we neglect higher-order terms, this results in

$$N_{xy}\frac{\partial^2 w}{\partial w\partial y}+\frac{\partial N_{xy}}{\partial x}\frac{\partial w}{\partial y}+N_{yx}\frac{\partial^2 w}{\partial x\partial y}+\frac{\partial N_{yx}}{\partial y}\frac{\partial w}{\partial x}$$

With all the above z components of forces per unit area evaluated, the governing plate equation can be modified to include their effect:

$$D\nabla^4 w=p(x,y)+N_x\frac{\partial^2 w}{\partial x^2}+N_y\frac{\partial^2 w}{\partial y^2}+2N_{xy}\frac{\partial^2 w}{\partial x\partial y}$$

$$+\frac{\partial N_x}{\partial x}\frac{\partial w}{\partial x}+\frac{\partial N_y}{\partial y}\frac{\partial w}{\partial y}$$

$$+\frac{\partial N_{xy}}{\partial x}\frac{\partial w}{\partial y}+\frac{\partial N_{yx}}{\partial y}\frac{\partial w}{\partial x}$$

However, from Equations (1.35) and (1.36), expressing the in-plane force equilibrium and the assumption that there are no applied surface shear stresses, it follows that

$$\frac{\partial N_x}{\partial x} + \frac{\partial N_{yx}}{\partial y} = 0$$

$$\frac{\partial N_{xy}}{\partial x} + \frac{\partial N_y}{\partial y} = 0$$

Substituting these into the expression above, the final form of the equation is found to be

$$D\nabla^4 w = p(x,y) + N_x \frac{\partial^2 w}{\partial x^2} + N_y \frac{\partial^2 w}{\partial y^2} + 2N_{xy} \frac{\partial^2 w}{\partial w \partial y} \qquad (5.3)$$

This equation is analogous to the beam-column equation, which can be obtained by multiplying Equation (5.3) by b (the width of the beam) and letting $\partial(\ )/\partial y = 0$, $\nu = 0$, $\bar{P} \equiv -bN_x$, and $q(x) = bp(x)$, to provide

$$\frac{d^4 w}{dx^4} + k^2 \frac{d^2 w}{\partial x^2} = \frac{q(x)}{EI}, \qquad \text{where} \quad k^2 = \frac{\bar{P}}{EI} \qquad (5.4)$$

It should be noted that the load $\bar{P}$ defined above is an in-plane load that when positive produces compressive stresses—a convention that differs from the one used elsewhere throughout this text. However, it is commonly used in the literature on buckling, and so we use it here, but put a bar on the P as a warning.

5.2. COLUMN BUCKLING

If we solve Equation (5.4) by the means described previously, the solution can be written as

$$w(x) = A\cos kx + B\sin kx + C + Dx + w_p(x)$$

where $w_p(x)$ is the particular solution for the loading $q(x)$. Consider the case wherein $q(x) = 0$ and the column is simply supported at each end. The boundary conditions at $x = 0, L$ are then

$$w(0) = w(L) = 0$$

$$M_x\left(\begin{array}{c} L \\ 0 \end{array}\right) = -EI\frac{d^2 w}{dx^2} = 0 \quad \text{or} \quad \frac{d^2 w(0)}{dx^2} = \frac{d^2 w(L)}{dx^2} = 0 \qquad (5.5)$$

From the first boundary condition, $A + C = 0$; from the third, $A = 0$; hence $C = 0$ also. From the second boundary condition, $B \sin kL + DL = 0$, and from the fourth boundary condition,

$$Bk^2 \sin kL = 0 = \frac{B\bar{P}}{EI} \sin kL = 0 \qquad (5.6)$$

Note that in Equation (5.6), if $kL \neq n\pi$ (n an integer), then $B = D = 0$; if $kl = n\pi$, then $D = 0$, whereas B is nonzero but indeterminate, and

$$\bar{P} = n^2 \pi^2 \frac{EI}{L^2} \qquad (5.7)$$

It is thus seen that for most values of the axial compressive loading $\bar{P}$, the lateral deflection w is zero ($A = B = C = D = 0$), and the in-plane and lateral forces and responses are uncoupled. However, for a countable infinity of discrete values of $\bar{P}$, there is a lateral deflection, and it is of an indeterminate magnitude. Mathematically, this situation is referred to as an eigenvalue problem, and the discrete values given in Equation (5.7) are called *eigenvalues*. The resulting deflections, in this case

$$w(x) = B \sin kx,$$

are called *eigenfunctions*.

The natural vibration of elastic bodies also gives rise to eigenvalue problems, in which the natural frequencies are the eigenvalues and the vibration modes are the eigenfunctions.

Returning to buckling, we see from Equation (5.7) that when $\bar{P}$ increases, the lowest buckling load occurs when $n = 1$. Hence $n > 1$ has no physical significance. The load

$$\bar{P} = \frac{\pi^2 EI}{L^2} \qquad (5.8)$$

is therefore the critical buckling load for this column under these boundary conditions. In this particular case the buckling load is called the Euler buckling load, after the Swiss mathematician who first studied the problem successfully.

Another way to formulate the buckling problem is exemplified by solving Equation 5.4, letting $q(x) = q_0 = \text{constant}$. The resulting particular solution is $q_0 x^2 / 2\bar{P}$. If the column is simply supported, one may solve the boundary-value problem for the lateral deflection; the result is

$$w(x) = \frac{q_0}{Pk^2 \sin kL} [\cos kx \sin kL + \sin kx - \cos kL - \sin kL$$

$$- Lx \sin kL + k^2 x^2 \sin kL] \tag{5.9}$$

In this solution, when the axial load $\bar{P}$ has the values given in Equation (5.7), $\sin kL = 0$, so that $w(x)$ goes to infinity—or more properly (since we have a small-deflection linear mathematical model), $w(x)$ becomes indefinitely large.

Hence, whether we solve the homogeneous Equation (5.4) (an eigenvalue problem), or the nonhomogeneous Equation (5.4), (a boundary-value problem), the results are identical: when $\bar{P}$ has values given by Equation (5.7), or physically where $\bar{P}$ attains the value given by Equation (5.8), the column buckles.

Note also that the buckling load, Equation (5.8), is not affected by any lateral load $q(x)$. The physical significance of a lateral load $q(x)$ is that the beam-column may deflect sufficiently, owing to the combination of lateral and in-plane compressive loads, that it fractures or yields prior to attaining the buckling load.

These elastic stability considerations are very important in analyzing or designing any structure in which compressive stresses result from the loading, because in addition to ensuring that the structure is not overstressed or overdeflected, in this case a new failure mode must be considered.

5.3. PLATE BUCKLING

Plate buckling is qualitatively analogous to column buckling, but the mathematics is more complicated, and the conditions that result in the lowest eigenvalue (the actual buckling load) are not so obvious in many cases.

Whenever the in-plane forces are compressive, and are more than a few percent of the plate buckling loads (to be defined later), Equation (5.3) must be used rather than Equation (5.1) in the analysis of plates.

For the plate, just as the case of the beam-column, the in-plane load that causes an elastic instability is not dependent upon the lateral load. Therefore, to investigate the elastic stability we assume $p(x,y) = 0$ in Equation (5.3).

Consider as an example a simply supported plate, subjected to constant in-plane loads N_x and N_y (let $N_{xy} = 0$), as shown in Figure 5.2 below. We assume the solution of Equation (5.3) be of the Navier form,

$$w(x,y) = \sum_{m=1}^{\infty} \sum_{n=1}^{\infty} A_{mn} \sin \frac{m\pi x}{a} \sin \frac{n\pi y}{b} \tag{5.10}$$

Substituting Equation (5.10) into Equation (5.3) and defining α to be

$$\alpha = \frac{N_y}{N_x} \tag{5.11}$$

we find the solution to this eigenvalue problem:

$$N_{x\,cr} = -D\pi^2 \frac{\left[(m/a)^2 + (n/b)^2 \right]^2}{(m/a)^2 + (n/b)^2 \alpha} \tag{5.12}$$

Here the subscript cr denotes that this is a critical load situation—the plate buckles. Also note that $N_{x\,cr}$ is a negative quantity, that is, a load that causes compressive stresses.

Equation (5.12) gives the complete set of eignevalues for the simply supported plate, analogous to Equation (5.7) for the column. In other words, for these discrete values of N_x and N_y, Equation (5.3) has nontrivial solutions wherein the lateral deflection is given by Equation (5.10); for other values $w(x,y) = 0$.

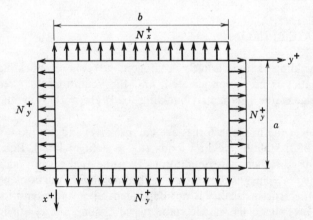

Fig. 5.2. Rectangular plate subjected to in-plane normal loads.

We know that as the load increases, the plate will buckle at the lowest buckling load (or eigenvalue), and all the rest of the eigenvalues have no physical meaning. What values of m and n (the numbers of half sine waves) make $N_{x\,\mathrm{cr}}$ a minimum?

Defining the length-to-width ratio $r = a/b$, we can rewrite Equation (5.12) as

$$N_{x\,\mathrm{cr}} = -\frac{D\pi^2}{a^2} \frac{\left[m^2 + n^2 r^2\right]^2}{m^2 + n^2 r^2 \alpha} \qquad (5.13)$$

Note: If in Equation (5.13) $\alpha = 0$, $r = 1$, and $m = n = 1$, then

$$N_{x\,\mathrm{cr}} = -\frac{4\pi^2 D}{a^2} \qquad (5.14)$$

Note also the similarities between Equations (5.14) and (5.8).

The question remains: given a combination of N_x and N_y loadings and a given geometry r, what values of m and n provide the lowest buckling loads? By manipulating Equation (5.13), one can make a plot such as Figure 5.3 below (which is not to scale) for a square plate ($a = b$, $r = 1$).

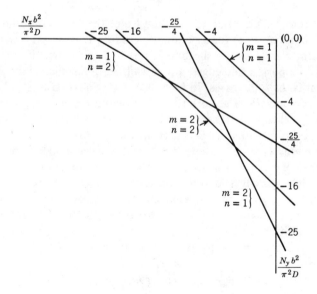

Fig. 5.3. Values of biaxial loads causing buckling for a square simply supported plate.

It is seen that such a plate, simply supported on all four edges, always buckles into a half sine wave ($m = n = 1$) under any combination of compressive N_x and N_y, since the line for those values of m and n is always closest to the origin, and thus corresponds to the lowest buckling load.

Next consider a plate under an in-plane load in the x direction only, so that $N_y = 0$ and $\alpha = 0$. In this case, Equation (5.12) can be written as

$$N_{x\,cr} = -\frac{D\pi^2 a^2}{m^2}\left[\frac{m^2}{a^2} + \frac{n^2}{b^2}\right]^2 \tag{5.15}$$

The loaded plate is shown in Sketch 5.3 below.

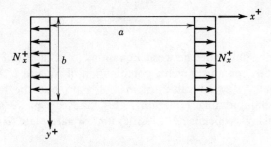

Sketch 5.3

Examination of Equation (5.15) shows that the first term is merely the Euler column load (5.8) for a column, including Poisson-ratio effects. The second term clearly shows the buckle-resisting effect that is provided by the simply supported side edges, and this effect diminishes as the plate gets wider, that is, as b increases. In fact, as $b \to \infty$, Equation (5.15) shows that the plate acts merely as an infinity of unit-width beams, simply supported at the ends, except that because they are "joined together," there is a Poisson-ratio effect; that is, D is used instead of EI.

It is obvious from Equation (5.15) that the minimum value of $N_{x\,cr}$ occurs when $n = 1$, since n appears only in the numerator. Thus for an isotropic plate, simply supported on all four edges, subjected only to a uniaxial in-plane load, the buckling mode given by Equation (5.10) will always be one half sine wave [$\sin(\pi y/b)$] across the span, regardless of the length or width of the plate.

Therefore, since $n = 1$, Equation (5.15) can be written as

$$N_{x\,cr} = -\frac{D\pi^2}{b^2}\left(\frac{m}{r} + \frac{r}{m}\right)^2 \tag{5.16}$$

where $r \equiv a/b$ as before.

Note if $a < b$ (the plate is wider than it is long), the second term is always less than the first; hence $N_{x\,\mathrm{min}}$ is always obtained by letting $m = 1$. Thus for $a < b$, the buckling mode for the simply supported plate is always

$$w(x,y) = A_{11} \sin \frac{\pi x}{a} \sin \frac{\pi y}{b}$$

In that case

$$N_{x\,\mathrm{cr}} = -\frac{D\pi^2}{b^2}\left(\frac{1}{r} + r\right)^2 \tag{5.17}$$

To find the aspect ratio r at which N_x is truly a minimum, we let

$$\frac{dN_{x\,\mathrm{cr}}}{dr} = 0 = -\frac{2D\pi^2}{b^2}\left(\frac{1}{r} + r\right)\left(-\frac{1}{r^2} + 1\right)$$

Therefore $r = 1$ provides that minimum value. Hence for $m = 1$, $N_{x\,\mathrm{cr}}$ has its minimum when $a = b$. Under that condition, from (5.17)

$$(N_{x\,\mathrm{cr}})_{a=b} = -\frac{4D\pi^2}{b^2} = -\frac{4D\pi^2}{a^2} \tag{5.18}$$

Comparing this with the Euler buckling load of Equation (5.8) for a simply supported column, we see that the continuity of a plate and the support along the sides of the plate provide a factor of at least 4 over a series of strips (columns) that are neither continuous nor supported along the unloaded edges.

Now as the length-to-width ratio a/b increases, the buckling load (5.17) will increase, and one can ask: Does $m = 1$ always result in the minimum buckling load, or is there another value of m that will provide a lower buckling load as r increases (e.g., $(N_{x\,\mathrm{cr}})_{m=2} \leqslant (N_{x\,\mathrm{cr}})_{m=1}$ for some r)?

Mathematically, this can be phrased as follows, using Equation (5.16):

$$\left(\frac{m}{r} + \frac{r}{m}\right)^2 \overset{?}{\leqslant} \left(\frac{m-1}{r} + \frac{r}{m-1}\right)^2$$

This states the condition under which a plate of aspect ratio r will buckle in m half sine waves in the loaded direction, rather than $m = 1$ sine waves. Manipulating this inequality results in

$$m(m-1) \leqslant r^2 \tag{5.19}$$

Thus the plate will buckle in two half sine waves in the axial direction rather than one when $r \geqslant \sqrt{2}$, in three rather than two when $r \geqslant \sqrt{6}$, and so on.

Again one can ask: When the plate buckles into the $m=2$ configuration, is there a minimum buckling load, and if so, at what r, and what is $(N_{x\,cr})_{\min}$?

From Equation (5.16),

$$\left(\frac{dN_{x\,cr}}{dr}\right)_{m=2} = 0 = -\frac{D\pi^2}{b^2}2\left(\frac{2}{r}+\frac{r}{2}\right)\left(-\frac{2}{r^2}+\frac{1}{2}\right) = 0$$

or $r^2 = 4, \qquad r = 2$

$$(N_{x\,cr})_{\min} = -\frac{4\pi^2 D}{b^2} \qquad \text{for} \quad m = 2 \tag{5.20}$$

This is the same value as given in Equation (5.18) for $m=1$. Proceeding with all values of r and m, the following graph (Figure 5.4) can be drawn, which clearly shows the results:

Hence if one knows the value of r, the figure provides the actual values of $N_{x\,cr}$ and m. However, in practice, for $r > 1$ one always simply uses Equation (5.18) or (5.20) for the buckling load, and there is usually little interest in the value of m.

However, looking more closely at Equation (5.19), we see that as m increases,

$$m(m-1) \to m^2 = r^2 \quad \text{or} \quad m = r = \frac{a}{b}$$

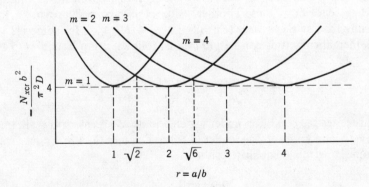

Fig. 5.4. Buckling load as a function of aspect ratio for a simply supported plate.

This says that for long plates, the half sine waves of the buckling have lengths approximately equal to the plate width. Another way of saying it is that a long plate simply supported on all four edges and subjected to a uniaxial compressive load tends to buckle into a number of square cells.

Remembering that $\sigma_x = N_x/h$, Equations (5.18) and (5.20) can be written as follows for $a/b \geqslant 1$:

$$\sigma_{cr} = -\frac{\pi^2 E}{3(1-\nu^2)}\left(\frac{h}{b}\right)^2 \tag{5.21}$$

The preceding discussion has been concerned with an isotropic plate simply supported on all four edges. To solve the governing differential equations for other boundary conditions results in equations for the eigenvalues that all too often are lengthy, complicated transcendental equations. They are difficult to use, and lack the clarity of those for a simply supported plate. Therefore, in most cases, for plates with other boundary conditions, energy methods are used to obtain approximate values for the buckling loads. This approach is treated in the next chapter.

5.4. REFERENCES

There are two references that provide a vast amount of design and analysis information on isotropic and orthotropic plates under most boundary conditions and loadings:

1. S. Timoshenko and J. Gere, *Theory of Elastic Stability*, 2nd ed. McGraw-Hill, 1961.
2. H.H. Bleich, *Buckling of Metal Structures*, McGraw-Hill, 1952.

5.5. PROBLEMS

5.1. In a plate with $\nu = 0.25$, clamped on all four edges and loaded in the x direction, the critical buckling stress is given by

$$\sigma_{cr} = -\frac{k\pi^2 D}{b^2 h} = -\frac{k\pi^2 E}{12(1-\nu^2)}\left(\frac{h}{b}\right)^2$$

where D is the flexural stiffness, b is the plate width, a is the plate length, h is the plate thickness, and k is given by*

* Portion of a table from *Theory of Elastic Stability* by S. Timoshenko and J. Gere. Copyright 1961, McGraw-Hill Book Company. Used with permission of McGraw-Hill Book Company.

a/b	0.75	1.0	1.5	2.0	2.5	3.0
k	11.69	10.07	8.33	7.88	7.57	7.37

(a) Part of a support fixture for a missile launcher measures 45 in. × 15 in., and must support 145,000 lb of axially compressive load. Its edges are all clamped. The plate is composed of aluminum with $E = 10 \times 10^6$ psi, $\sigma_{allowable} = \pm 30,000$ psi (both the tensile and the compressive allowable stress are of magnitude 30,000 psi, and $\nu = 0.25$. What thickness is required to prevent buckling? What thickness is required to prevent overstressing?

(b) Suppose a steel plate of the same dimensions is used instead of the aluminum, with the following properties: $E_{steel} = 30 \times 10^6$ psi, $\nu = 0.25$, and $\sigma_{allowable} = \pm 100,000$ psi. What thickness is needed to prevent buckling? Would the steel plate be overstressed with that thickness?

(c) The density of steel is 0.283 lb/in.^{3}; the density of aluminum is 0.100 lb/in.^{3} Which plate will be lighter?

5.2.   A structural component in the interior of an underwater structure consists of a square plate of dimension a simply supported on all four sides. If the component is subjected to in-plane compressive loads in both the x and y directions of equal magnitude, find $N_{x\,cr}$.

5.3.   An aluminum support structure consists of a rectangular plate simply supported on all four edges and is subjected to an in-plane uniaxial compressive load. If the length of the plate in the load direction is 4 ft and the width 3 ft, determine the minimum plate thickness to ensure that the plate would buckle in the elastic range, if the material properties are $E = 10 \times 10^6$ psi, $\nu = 0.3$, and the compressive yield stress $\sigma_y = -30,000$ psi.

6

ENERGY METHODS

As an alternative to developing the governing differential equations for a material point in an elastic body and solving them for a specified loading and certain boundary conditions, as has been done in the first five chapters, one can develop an expression for the strain energy in an elastic body and the work done by forces acting on the body, and obtain solutions from this expression instead. In solid mechanics, there are three primary energy methods, based on minimum potential energy, minimum complementary energy, and Reissner's variational theorem. In his mechanics-of-materials course the student usually learns of minimum potential energy, perhaps through the name of virtual work; Castigliano's theorem is an example of minimum complementary energy; and few at this level are familiar with Reissner's theorem. Only the first of these methods is treated here.

6.1. MINIMUM POTENTIAL ENERGY

For an elastic body, the potential energy can be written as

$$V = \int_R W\,dR - \int_{S_t} T_i u_i\,dS - \int_R F_i u_i\,dR \qquad (6.1)$$

where

W = strain-energy-density function

R = volume of the elastic body

T_i = ith component of the surface traction

u_i = ith component of the deformation

F_i = ith component of the body force

S_t = portion of the surface over which tractions are prescribed.

The first term on the right-hand side is the strain energy of the body. The second and third terms are the work done by the surface tractions and the body forces, respectively.

The theorem of minimum potential energy states[1]:

"Of all displacements satisfying the given boundary conditions those which satisfy the equilibrium equations make the potential energy an absolute minimum."*

Mathematically, this condition can be written as

$$\delta V = 0 \qquad (6.2)$$

Here the lower-case delta represents a mathematical operation called variation. Operationally, it is analogous to partial differentiation, and to

* From *Mathematical Theory of Elasticity* by I. S. Sokolnikoff. Copyright 1956, McGraw-Hill Book Company. Used with permission of McGraw-Hill Book Company.

solve problems in structural mechanics only the following two properties are needed:

$$\frac{d(\delta y)}{dx} = \delta\left(\frac{dy}{dx}\right), \qquad \delta(y^2) = 2y\,\delta y \tag{6.3}$$

For the case of elastic stability, neglecting body forces and substituting Equation (6.1) into Equation (6.2), one sees that

$$\delta V = \delta\left[\int_R w\,dR - \int_{S_t} T_i u_i\,dS\right] = 0 \tag{6.4}$$

One way to interpret this is that the potential energy of the elastic body does not change (i.e., the variation in potential energy is zero) when the body passes from a configuration of equilibrium (prior to buckling) to an infinitesimally near adjacent configuration (after buckling). One then seeks the forces T_i that will cause such a situation to occur. Some refer to the theorem, stated in this manner, as the theorem of stationary potential energy.

The strain-energy-density function W is defined as

$$W \equiv \tfrac{1}{2}\sigma_{ij}\varepsilon_{ij} \tag{6.5}$$

For a body described in a Cartesian coordinate frame, Equation (6.5) is written as

$$W = \tfrac{1}{2}\sigma_x\varepsilon_x + \tfrac{1}{2}\sigma_y\varepsilon_y + \tfrac{1}{2}\sigma_z\varepsilon_z + \sigma_{xy}\varepsilon_{xy} + \sigma_{xz}\varepsilon_{xz} + \sigma_{yz}\varepsilon_{yz} \tag{6.6}$$

To utilize the theorem of minimum potential energy, it is necessary to express the strain-energy-density function in terms of displacements.

Furthermore, if (for example) one wishes to obtain the strain energy for a plate, then one makes use of all of the plate-theory assumptions in developing the strain-energy relationship, namely,

$$\sigma_z = \varepsilon_z = \varepsilon_{xz} = \varepsilon_{yz} = 0$$

$$u = u_0(x,y) + z\alpha(x,y), \qquad \text{where} \quad \alpha = -\frac{\partial w}{\partial x} \tag{6.7}$$

$$v = v_0(x,y) + z\beta(x,y), \qquad \text{where} \quad \beta = -\frac{\partial w}{\partial y}$$

From Equations (1.4), (1.5), and (1.7), using Equation (6.7) above, one obtains

$$\sigma_x = \frac{E}{1 - \nu^2} \left[\varepsilon_x + \nu \varepsilon_y \right]$$

$$\sigma_y = \frac{E}{1 - \nu^2} \left[\varepsilon_y + \nu \varepsilon_x \right] \qquad (6.8)$$

$$\sigma_{xy} = \frac{E}{1 + \nu} \varepsilon_{xy}$$

Substituting Equations (6.8) and (6.7) into Equation (6.6) results in

$$W = \frac{E}{2(1 - \nu^2)} \varepsilon_x \left[\varepsilon_x + \nu \varepsilon_y \right] + \frac{E}{2(1 - \nu^2)} \varepsilon_y \left[\varepsilon_y + \nu \varepsilon_x \right] + \frac{E}{1 + \nu} \varepsilon_{xy}^2 \quad (6.9)$$

Now for a plate subjected to bending and stretching, the deflection assumptions are, of course,

$$u = u_0 - z \frac{\partial w}{\partial x}, \qquad v = v_0 - z \frac{\partial w}{\partial y}, \qquad w = w(x,y)$$

The strain-energy-density function [Equation (6.9)] therefore becomes

$$W = \frac{1}{2} \frac{E}{1 - \nu^2} \left\{ \left(\frac{\partial u_0}{\partial x} \right)^2 + \left(\frac{\partial v_0}{\partial y} \right)^2 + 2\nu \left(\frac{\partial u_0}{\partial x} \right) \left(\frac{\partial v_0}{\partial y} \right) + \frac{1 - \nu}{2} \left[\frac{\partial u_0}{\partial y} + \frac{\partial v_0}{\partial x} \right]^2 \right\}$$

$$+ \frac{Ez^2}{2(1 - \nu^2)} \left[\left(\frac{\partial^2 w}{\partial x^2} \right)^2 + \left(\frac{\partial^2 w}{\partial y^2} \right)^2 + 2\nu \left(\frac{\partial^2 w}{\partial x^2} \right) \left(\frac{\partial^2 w}{\partial y^2} \right) \right]$$

$$+ \frac{E(1 - \nu)z^2}{1 - \nu^2} \left(\frac{\partial^2 w}{\partial x \partial y} \right)^2 \qquad (6.10)$$

The strain energy $U \left(= \int_R W \, dR \right)$ can then be found, and it is seen that in Equation (6.10) u_0, v_0, and w are not functions of z. Hence one can easily integrate with respect to z, with the result

$$U = \frac{K}{2} \int_0^a \int_0^b \left\{ \left(\frac{\partial u_0}{\partial x} + \frac{\partial v_0}{\partial y} \right)^2 - 2(1-\nu) \frac{\partial u_0}{\partial x} \frac{\partial v_0}{\partial y} \right.$$

$$\left. + \frac{(1-\nu)}{2} \left(\frac{\partial u_0}{\partial y} + \frac{\partial v_0}{\partial x} \right)^2 \right\} dx\, dy + \frac{D}{2} \int_0^a \int_0^b \left\{ \left(\frac{\partial^2 w}{\partial x^2} + \frac{\partial^2 w}{\partial y^2} \right)^2 \right.$$

$$\left. - 2(1-\nu) \left[\left(\frac{\partial^2 w}{\partial x^2} \right) \left(\frac{\partial^2 w}{\partial y^2} \right) - \left(\frac{\partial^2 w}{\partial x \partial y} \right)^2 \right] \right\} dx\, dy \qquad (6.11)$$

It is seen that the first term in the bending strain energy is proportional to the square of the average plate curvature. The second term is known as the Gaussian curvature.

In Equation (6.5), by using other appropriate assumptions on stresses, strains, and form of displacements, one can obtain the strain-energy expression for a beam, ring, shell, and so on.

Returning to Equation (6.1), consider a plate subjected to a lateral loading $p(x,y)$ and in-plane loads N_x, N_y, and N_{xy}, in order to study the problem of plate buckling discussed in Chapter 5.

For the lateral loading $p(x,y)$ it is clear that the work done is

$$\int_{S_t} T_i u_i\, dS = \int_0^a \int_0^b p(x,y) w(x,y)\, dx\, dy \qquad (6.12)$$

To obtain the work done by the in-plane forces in deformation prior to buckling as well as buckling deformations, it is necessary to employ the first two terms of the expansion of strains in terms of displacements, namely:

$$\varepsilon_x = \frac{\partial u_o}{\partial x} + \frac{1}{2} \left(\frac{\partial w}{\partial x} \right)^2$$

$$\varepsilon_y = \frac{\partial v_o}{\partial y} + \frac{1}{2} \left(\frac{\partial w}{\partial y} \right)^2 \qquad (6.13)$$

$$\varepsilon_{xy} = \frac{1}{2} \left(\frac{\partial u_o}{\partial y} + \frac{\partial v_o}{\partial x} \right) + \frac{1}{2} \frac{\partial w}{\partial x} \frac{\partial w}{\partial y}$$

This includes a nonlinear term not considered before, but necessary in order to couple the effect of the in-plane load to the resulting lateral deflection w. This is analogous to the modifications of the plate equations in Section 5.1. In Equation (6.13) the first term on the right-hand side of each equation reflects the deformation caused by the stretching (or compressing) of the midsurface of the plate under the in-plane loads, which is the minimum-energy mode of deformation up to the value of the buckling load. The second term reflects the lateral deformations $w(x,y)$ that occur when the in-plane loads reach the buckling load, and where there is no stretching or shortening of the plate middle surface ($u_0 = v_0 = 0$). Hence the complete expression for the work done under the action of in-plane loads is

$$\int_{S_t} T_i u_i \, ds = - \int_0^a \int_0^b \left\{ N_x \left[\frac{\partial u_o}{\partial x} + \frac{1}{2} \left(\frac{\partial w}{\partial x} \right)^2 \right] \right.$$

$$+ N_y \left[\frac{\partial v_o}{\partial y} + \frac{1}{2} \left(\frac{\partial w}{\partial y} \right)^2 \right]$$

$$\left. + N_{xy} \left[\left(\frac{\partial u_o}{\partial y} + \frac{\partial v_o}{\partial x} \right) + \left(\frac{\partial w}{\partial x} \right) \left(\frac{\partial w}{\partial y} \right) \right] \right\} dx \, dy \qquad (6.14)$$

If one is seeking only buckling loads (i.e., in this case, loads that cause lateral deflections only) one should set $u_0 = v_0 = 0$ in Equations (6.11) and (6.14). Note that the minus sign in Equation (6.14) occurs solely because N_x, N_y are tensile stress resultants; also that N_{xy} is defined consistently with N_x and N_y, as in Section 5.1.

To summarize: If one is investigating the buckling of a plate in the presence of lateral loads, the potential energy is written (remembering that the buckling load is independent of the lateral loads) as

$$V = \frac{D}{2} \int_0^a \int_0^b \left\{ \left(\frac{\partial^2 w}{\partial x^2} + \frac{\partial^2 w}{\partial y^2} \right)^2 - 2(1-\nu) \left[\left(\frac{\partial^2 w}{\partial x^2} \right) \left(\frac{\partial^2 w}{\partial y^2} \right) \right. \right.$$

$$\left. \left. - \left(\frac{\partial^2 w}{\partial x \partial y} \right)^2 \right] \right\} dx \, dy - \int_0^a \int_0^b p(x,y) w(x,y) \, dx \, dy$$

$$+ \frac{1}{2} \int_0^a \int_0^b \left[N_x \left(\frac{\partial w}{\partial x} \right)^2 + N_y \left(\frac{\partial w}{\partial y} \right)^2 + 2 N_{xy} \left(\frac{\partial w}{\partial x} \right) \left(\frac{\partial w}{\partial y} \right) \right] dx\, dy. \quad (6.15)$$

One can use the theorem of minimum potential energy in three ways. First, one can use it to obtain governing equations and the natural boundary conditions for a problem that is consistent with the assumptions made in obtaining the strain-energy expression. Second, if one knows what the deformation pattern is under the loads, except for an amplitude, then by substituting the displacement function into Equation (6.15) one can obtain the actual amplitude of the deformation caused by a lateral load $p(x,y)$, or the values of the critical loading ($N_{x\mathrm{cr}}$, $N_{y\mathrm{cr}}$ or $N_{xy\mathrm{cr}}$. Third, if one does not know the form of the deformation exactly but can make a good estimate, then one can use the theorem to obtain approximate deformations due to $p(x,y)$ or approximate values of buckling loads. By far the most useful of these to engineers is the third application.

Each of these applications is now demonstrated, and to maintain simplicity and lucidity, the first two are illustrated with a beam.

6.2. THE BENDING OF A BEAM DUE TO A LATERAL LOAD

Consider a beam of length a and width b, where as before the displacement and load are functions of the length coordinate x only. Without in-plane loads, Equation (6.15) can be written as

$$V = \frac{EI}{2} \int_0^a \left(\frac{d^2 w}{dx^2} \right)^2 dx - \int_0^a q(x) w(x)\, dx \quad (6.16)$$

where $\quad q(x) = bp(x)$

$$I = \frac{bh^3}{12} \quad \text{(remember that for a beam } \nu = 0\text{)}.$$

We now use the theorem of minimum potential energy to obtain the governing differential equation and the natural boundary conditions for a beam under lateral loading. From Equation (6.2),

$$\delta V = 0 = \frac{EI}{2} \int_0^a \delta \left(\frac{d^2 w}{dx^2} \right)^2 dx - \int_0^a q(x)\, \delta w\, dx \quad (6.17)$$

To solve for the governing equation, the first term on the right-hand side must be integrated by parts several times. The details of the process are:

$$\frac{EI}{2} \int_0^a \delta \left(\frac{d^2w}{dx^2} \right)^2 dx = EI \int_0^a \left(\frac{d^2w}{dx^2} \right) \delta \left(\frac{d^2w}{dx^2} \right) dx$$

$$= EI \int_0^a \frac{d^2w}{dx^2} \frac{d^2}{dx^2} (\delta w) \, dx = \left[\left(EI \frac{d^2w}{dx^2} \right) \delta \left(\frac{dw}{dx} \right) \right]_0^a - EI \int_0^a \frac{d^3w}{dx^3} \frac{d}{dx} (\delta w) \, dx$$

$$= \left[\left(EI \frac{d^2w}{dx^2} \right) \delta \left(\frac{dw}{dx} \right) \right]_0^a - \left[\left(EI \frac{d^3w}{dx^3} \right) \delta w \right]_0^a + EI \int_0^a \frac{d^4w}{dx^4} \delta w \, dx \qquad (6.18)$$

Substituting Equation (6.18) into Equation (6.17) and rearranging, one obtains

$$\delta V = 0 = \left[\left(EI \frac{d^2w}{dx^2} \right) \delta \left(\frac{dw}{dx} \right) \right]_0^a - \left[\left(EI \frac{d^3w}{dx^3} \right) \delta w \right]_0^a$$

$$+ \int_0^a \left[EI \frac{d^4w}{dx^4} - q(x) \right] \delta w \, dx = 0. \qquad (6.19)$$

For this to be true, the following equation must be true:

$$EI \frac{d^4w}{dx^4} = q(x) \qquad (6.20)$$

It is seen that this is the governing differential equation for a beam. Obviously, there are other approaches that could have been used to obtain this well-known equation. However, if analyzing a structure or elastic body that is not one of the classical shapes, then by making use of physical intuition or experience, or by performing experiments, an engineer can make certain assumptions on displacements, strains, and stresses, and then utilize the theorem of minimum potential energy to develop one or more governing equations for the problem.

When one uses a variational principle in this way, the resulting differential equations are called the Euler-Lagrange equations.

Looking also at Equation (6.19), one sees that several natural boundary conditions are specified. The first term on the right-hand side implies that at each end of the beam $(x=0,a)$,

Either $\quad M_x = -EI\dfrac{d^2w}{dx^2} = 0 \quad$ or $\quad \dfrac{dw}{dx}$ must be specified $\qquad$ (6.21)

That is, the variation of dw/dx is 0.

Likewise, from the second term, at the ends of the beam $(x=0,a)$,

Either $\quad V_x = -EI\dfrac{d^3w}{dx^3} = 0 \quad$ or $\quad w$ must be specified $\qquad$ (6.22)

It is easily seen that these natural boundary conditions include for the beam all the classical boundary conditions: simply supported, clamped, free, and spring-supported.

Again, when analyzing difficult elasticity problems through the use of minimum potential energy, not only does one obtain an Euler-Lagrange equation that is consistent with the assumptions adopted, but one also obtains sets of natural boundary conditions consistent with the same assumptions. This can be of great utility in "real life" problems.

6.3. THE BUCKLING OF A SIMPLY SUPPORTED COLUMN DUE TO AN AXIAL LOAD

To illustrate the second use of the theorem of minimum potential energy, consider a beam of length a, width b, wherein displacements vary only in the x direction, and which is subjected to an axial load N_x. Suppose one assumes that the column responds to the load N_x by assuming the following deflection shape:

$$w(x) = A \sin \frac{\pi x}{a} \qquad (6.23)$$

From Equation (6.15) the potential-energy expression is seen to be

$$V = \frac{EI}{2} \int_0^a \left(\frac{d^2w}{dx^2}\right)^2 dx + \frac{1}{2} \int_0^a P\left(\frac{dw}{dx}\right)^2 dx \qquad (6.24)$$

where $\quad P = N_x b$ (lb).

Substituting Equation (6.23) into (6.24) results in

$$V = \frac{EI}{2} A^2 \frac{\pi^4}{a^4} \int_0^a \sin^2 \left(\frac{\pi x}{a} \right) dx + \frac{1}{2} PA^2 \frac{\pi^2}{a^2} \int_0^a \cos^2 \left(\frac{\pi x}{a} \right) dx$$

$$= \frac{A^2}{2} \frac{\pi^2}{a^2} \frac{a}{2} \left[\frac{EI\pi^2}{a^2} + P \right] \tag{6.25}$$

Now using Equation (6.2) it is seen that in Equations (6.23) and (6.25) the function of x was prescribed, and the only symbol that can have a variation is the amplitude A. Hence

$$\delta V = 0 = \frac{a\pi^2}{4a^2} 2A \, \delta A \left[\frac{\pi^2 EI}{a^2} + P \right] = 0$$

For this to be true, it is required that

$$P_{cr} = - \frac{\pi^2 EI}{a^2} \tag{6.26}$$

This then is the value of the load P that causes the assumed deformation (6.23). Since, however, Equation (6.23) describes the exact buckling mode for a simply supported column, the load is also exactly the Euler buckling load obtained previously.

Hence in using minimum potential energy, for any elastic body, if one assumes the exact form of the deformation by design or happenstance, one then obtains the exact value of the buckling load in the eigenvalue problem or the exact amplitude of the deformation in a boundary-value problem.

However, the most beneficial use of the energy theorem occurs when one cannot formulate a suitable set of governing differential equations, when one cannot guess the deformation pattern, or when one cannot ascertain a consistent set of boundary conditions. In that case one can make a reasonable assumption for the displacements, and then find an approximate solution. This is illustrated in the following section.

6.4. THE BUCKLING UNDER UNIAXIAL LOAD OF A PLATE SIMPLY SUPPORTED ON THREE SIDES, AND FREE ON AN UNLOADED EDGE

Consider the plate shown in Sketch 6.1 below.

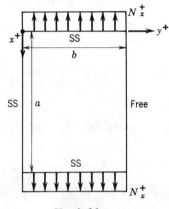

Sketch 6.1

The governing differential equation is obtained from Equation (5.3):

$$\frac{\partial^4 w}{\partial x^4} + 2\frac{\partial^4 w}{\partial x^2 \partial y^2} + \frac{\partial^4 w}{\partial y^4} = \frac{N_x}{D}\frac{\partial^2 w}{\partial x^2} \tag{6.27}$$

To solve for the buckling load directly, a Levy-type solution may be assumed:

$$w(x,y) = \sum_{m=1}^{\infty} \Psi_m(y)\sin\frac{m\pi x}{a} \tag{6.28}$$

Substituting Equation (6.28) into Equation (6.27) results in the following ordinary differential equation to solve:

$$\lambda_m^4 \Psi - 2\lambda_m^2 \Psi'' + \Psi^{IV} = -\frac{N_x}{D}\lambda_m^2 \Psi \tag{6.29}$$

where $\quad \lambda_m = \dfrac{m\pi}{a}$, $(\,)'' = \dfrac{d^2(\,)}{dy^2}$, and $(\,)^{IV} = \dfrac{d^4(\,)}{dy^4}$.

Letting $\overline{N}_x = -N_x$, we can solve Equation (6.29), with the result

$$\Psi_m(y) = A\cosh\alpha y + B\sinh\alpha y + C\cos\beta y + E\sin\beta y \tag{6.30}$$

where

$$\alpha = \left[\lambda_m^2 + \lambda_m \sqrt{\frac{\overline{N}_{xm}}{D}} \right]^{1/2}$$

$$\beta = \left[-\lambda_m^2 + \lambda_m \sqrt{\frac{\overline{N}_{xm}}{D}} \right]^{1/2}$$

The boundary conditions on the $y = 0$ and b edges are

$$w(x,0) = 0 \Rightarrow \Psi(0) = 0$$

$$M_y(x,0) = 0 \Rightarrow \Psi''(0) = 0$$

$$M_y(x,b) = 0 \Rightarrow \Psi''(b) - \nu\lambda_m^2\Psi(b) = 0$$

$$V_y(x,b) = 0 \Rightarrow \Psi'''(b) - (2-\nu)\lambda_m^2\Psi'(b) = 0 \qquad (6.31)$$

It is clear that the first two boundary conditions require that $A = C = 0$. Satisfying the other two boundary conditions results in the following relationship for the eigenvalue (i.e., the buckling load $\overline{N}_{xm} = -N_x$):

$$-\beta \tanh \alpha b \left[\alpha^2 - \nu\lambda_m^2 \right]^2 + \alpha \tan \beta b \left[\beta^2 + \nu\lambda_m^2 \right]^2 = 0 \qquad (6.32)$$

Thus knowing the plate geometry and the material properties, one can solve for the buckling loads for each value of m. It can be shown that the minimum buckling load will occur for $m = 1$, so that the deflection is a half sine wave in the longitudinal direction. However, note the complexity both in obtaining Equation (6.32), and then in using that equation to obtain the buckling load, in comparison with the relative simplicity of Section 5.3 in solving the simpler problem of the plate simply supported on all four edges. The solutions of this problem have been catalogued by Timoshenko and Gere[2] and are given below:*

* Portion of a table from *Theory of Elastic Stability* by S. Timoshenko and J. Gere. Copyright 1961, McGraw-Hill Book Company. Used with permission of McGraw-Hill Book Company.

$$-N_x = R_x = \frac{k\pi^2 D}{b^2}, \quad \text{or} \quad \sigma_{cr} = -\frac{k\pi^2 E}{12(1-\nu^2)}\left(\frac{h}{b}\right)^2, \quad \nu = 0.25 \quad (6.33)$$

a/b	0.50	1.0	2.0	3.0	4.0	5.0
k	4.40	1.44	0.698	0.564	0.516	0.506

Now we solve the same problem using the theorem of minimum potential energy. However, before doing so a brief discussion regarding boundary conditions is in order. They can be divided into two categories: geometric and stress. Geometric boundary conditions involve the specification of the displacement function and its first derivative—for example, the lateral displacement w or the slope at the boundary ($\partial w/\partial x$ or $\partial w/\partial y$). Stress boundary conditions involve the specification of the second and third derivatives of the displacement function, such as the stress couples M_x, M_y, M_{xy}, or the transverse shear resultants Q_x, Q_y, or the effective transverse shear resultants V_x, V_y discussed in Chapter 1.

In using the minimum-potential-energy theorem one must choose a deflection function that *at least* satisfies the specified *geometric* boundary conditions. This function will give a reasonable approximate solution. Better yet, by assuming a deflection function that satisfies all specified boundary conditions, one can achieve a very good approximate solution. If one could choose a deflection function that satisfied all boundary conditions and the governing differential equation for the problem also, this would of course be the exact solution. Finally, if one chose a deflection function that did not satisfy even the geometric boundary conditions, the solution would be inaccurate, because in effect the solution would not be for the problem to be solved, but for some other problem for which the assumed deflection did satisfy the geometric boundary conditions.

In this example, the following function is assumed for the lateral deflection:

$$w(x,y) = Ay \sin \frac{\pi x}{a} \quad (6.34)$$

This satisfies all boundary conditions on the $x = 0, a$ edges. It satisfies the geometric boundary condition that $w(x,0) = 0$, but does not satisfy the stress boundary conditions that $M_y(x,b) = V_y(x,b) = 0$. Substituting Equation (6.34) and its derivatives into Equation (6.15), where of course $N_y = N_{xy} = p(x,y) = 0$, produces

$$V = \frac{D}{2} \int_0^a \int_0^b \left\{ \left[-Ay\frac{\pi^2}{a^2} \sin\frac{\pi x}{a} \right]^2 + 2(1-\nu)\left[A\frac{\pi}{a} \cos\frac{\pi x}{a} \right]^2 \right\} dx\, dy$$

$$+ \frac{N_x}{2} \int_0^a \int_0^b A^2 y^2 \frac{\pi^2}{a^2} \cos^2\frac{\pi x}{a} dx\, dy \tag{6.35}$$

Integrating Equation (6.35) gives

$$V = A^2 D\left[\frac{\pi^4}{a^3}\frac{b^3}{3} + 2(1-\nu)\frac{\pi^2 b}{a} \right] + N_x A^2 \frac{\pi^2 b^3}{3a}.$$

Setting $\delta V = 0$, where the only variable with which to take a variation is A, produces the requirement that

$$N_x = -\left[\frac{\pi^2 D}{a^2} + \frac{6(1-\nu)D}{b^2} \right] \tag{6.36}$$

To compare this approximate result with the exact solution shown previously, let $a/b = 1$ and $\nu = 0.25$. From Equation (6.36),

$$N_x = -1.456\frac{\pi^2 D}{b^2} \tag{6.37}$$

In the exact solution the coefficient is 1.440. Hence the difference between the approximate solution and the exact solution is only about 1%, yet the three stress boundary conditions on the $y = $ constant edges were not satisfied.

6.5. SOME GENERAL REMARKS

Thus the minimum-potential-energy principle can be used for determining buckling loads, using assumed deflection functions that satisfy all boundary conditions, with a resultant saving in labor, yet producing very accurate results.

It should be noted that assuming a deflection function that satisfies only the geometric boundary conditions sometimes results in buckling loads that are less accurate. Also, it can be proven that the use of an approximate deformation function always produces buckling loads that are *higher* than the exact solution. Likewise, note that the potential energy can be used with Hamilton's principle to obtain approximate values of natural frequencies. Mathematically this can be expressed as

$$I = \int_{t_1}^{t_2} (T - V)\, dt$$

$$\delta I = 0$$

where T is the kinetic energy of the structure, and V is the potential energy used in this chapter.

Lastly, the use of energy theorems and variational principles to obtain solutions for plates composed of composite materials is treated in detail by Vinson and Chou.[3]

6.6. REFERENCES

1. I. S. Sokolnikoff, *Mathematical Theory of Elasticity*, 2nd ed., McGraw-Hill, 1956.
2. S. Timoshenko and J. Gere, *Theory of Elastic Stability*, 2nd ed., McGraw-Hill, 1961.
3. J. R. Vinson and T. W. Chou, *Composite Materials and Their Use in Structures*, Applied Science Publishers, 1974.

6.7. PROBLEMS

6.1. Consider a steel plate ($E = 30 \times 10^6$ psi, $\nu = 0.25$, $\sigma_y = 30{,}000$ psi) used as a portion of a bulkhead on a ship. The bulkhead is 60 in. long and 30 in. wide, and is subjected to an in-plane compressive load in the longer direction. What thickness must the plate be to have a buckling stress equal to the yield stress if
(a) The plate is simply supported on all four edges?
(b) The plate is simply supported on three edges and free on one unloaded edge?

6.2. Given a column of width b, height h, and length L, simply supported at each end, use the principle of minimum potential energy to determine the buckling load, if one assumes the deflection to be

(a) $\quad w(x) = A \dfrac{x}{L}(L - x)$

(b) $\quad w(x) = \dfrac{A}{L^3}[2Lx^3 - x^4 - L^3x]$

where in each case A is an amplitude.

Do the deflections assumed above satisfy the geometric boundary conditions? Do they satisfy the stress boundary conditions?

6.3. Consider the plates in Sketch 6.2 below, each subjected to a uniform axial compressive load $\overline{N}_x = -N_x$ (lb/in.) in the x direction. Determine a suitable deflection function $w(x,y)$ in each case for subsequent use in the principle of minimum potential energy to determine the critical load $\overline{N}_x$.

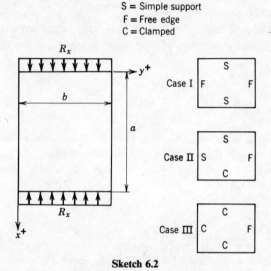

Sketch 6.2

6.4. For an end plate in a support structure with the boundary conditions in Sketch 6.3 use the principle of minimum potential energy to determine the buckling load, if one assumes the deflection function to be $w = Ay[1 - \cos(2\pi x/a)]$.

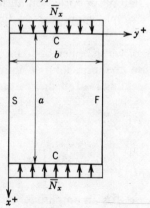

Sketch 6.3

6.5. Consider a rectangular plate determined by $0 \leqslant x \leqslant a$, $0 \leqslant y \leqslant b$, $-h/2 \leqslant z \leqslant h/2$. If the lateral deflection $w(x,y)$ is assumed to be in a separable form $w = f(x)g(y)$, and if $w = 0$ on all boundaries, determine the amount of strain energy due to the terms comprising the Gaussian curvature.

6.6. The base of a missile launch platform consists in part of vertical rectangular plates of height a and width b, where $a > b$. They are tied into the foundation below and the platform above in such a way that those edges can be considered clamped. However, on their vertical edges they are tied into I beams, so that those edges can only be considered simply supported. Using the theorem of minimum potential energy, derive the equation for the buckling load per inch of edge distance, $N_{x\,cr}$, for these plates, using a suitable deflection function, so that the plates can be designed to resist buckling.

6.7. An alternative to the design of Problem 6.6 would be to stiffen the vertical support beams so that the plate members can be considered to have their vertical edges clamped. Thus the plates have all four edges clamped. Employing a suitable deflection function, use the theorem of minimum potential energy to determine an expression for the critical buckling load per unit edge distance, $N_{x\,cr}$, to use in designing the plates. Is the plate with all edges clamped thicker or thinner than the one with the sides simply supported by Problem 6.6, if it is to have the same buckling load?

6.8. The legs of a water tower consist of three columns of length a and constant flexural stiffness EI, simply supported at one end and clamped at the other end. Using the theorem of minimum potential energy and a suitable function for the lateral deflection, calculate the buckling load P_{cr} for the legs, in order that they may be properly designed.

7

CYLINDRICAL SHELLS

7.1. CYLINDRICAL SHELLS UNDER GENERAL LOADS

The simplest of all shell geometries is that of the circular cylindrical shell shown in Sketch 7.1.

The positive values of all stress-resultant and stress-couple quantities are shown on the element in Sketch 7.2.

In shell theory, one uses all the assumptions used in the plate-theory derivation of Chapter 1, such as

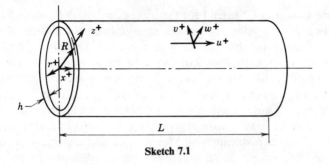

Sketch 7.1

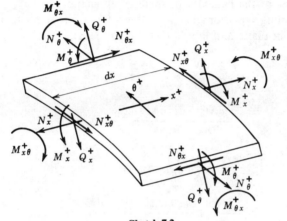

Sketch 7.2

$$\sigma_z = \varepsilon_z = \varepsilon_{zx} = \varepsilon_{z\theta} = 0$$

$$u = u_0(x,\theta) + \beta_x(x,\theta)z$$

$$v = v_0(x,\varepsilon) + \beta_\theta(x,\theta)z$$

$$w = w(x,\theta) \tag{7.1}$$

In addition there is another condition, known as Love's first approximation, which is consistent with the neglect of transverse shear deformation, and is written as

$$\frac{h}{R} \ll 1 \tag{7.2}$$

To derive the governing equations for cylindrical shells properly, one should begin with the equations of elasticity in a curvilinear coordinate system, just as we began with the elasticity equations in a Cartesian coordinate system in Chapter 1 for the plate-equation derivation. Then one could proceed to develop the governing equations for a shell of general shape, then specialize the equations to a shell of revolution, and finally specialize them to a shell of circular cylindrical geometry. To do this properly would require another two chapters, two weeks of lectures, and a knowledge of curvilinear coordinate systems; hence it is not done rigorously here. Those interested should take a graduate course in shell theory. In what follows, please accept the governing equations as correct, and regard them as a starting point for the detailed treatment of solutions for circular cylindrical shells, and more generally, a means to a better understanding of the behavior of shells of all shapes.

The governing equations are as follows for a circular cylindrical shell subjected to in-plane and lateral distributed loads:

$$\frac{\partial N_x}{\partial x} + \frac{1}{R}\frac{\partial N_{x\theta}}{\partial \theta} + q_x = 0 \tag{7.3}$$

$$\frac{\partial N_{x\theta}}{\partial x} + \frac{1}{R}\frac{\partial N_\theta}{\partial \theta} + \frac{Q_\theta}{R} + q_\theta = 0 \tag{7.4}$$

$$\frac{\partial Q_x}{\partial x} + \frac{1}{R}\frac{\partial Q_\theta}{\partial \theta} - \frac{1}{R}N_\theta + p(x,\theta) = 0 \tag{7.5}$$

$$\frac{\partial M_x}{\partial x} + \frac{1}{R}\frac{\partial M_{x\theta}}{\partial \theta} - (Q_x - m_x) = 0 \tag{7.6}$$

$$\frac{\partial M_{x\theta}}{\partial x} + \frac{1}{R}\frac{\partial M_\theta}{\partial \theta} - (Q_\theta - m_\theta) = 0 \tag{7.7}$$

$$\beta_x + \frac{\partial w}{\partial x} = 0 \tag{7.8}$$

$$\beta_\theta + \frac{1}{R}\frac{\partial w}{\partial \theta} - \frac{v_o}{R} = 0 \tag{7.9}$$

$$N_x = K\left[\frac{\partial u_o}{\partial x} + \frac{v}{R}\frac{\partial v_o}{\partial \theta} + \frac{v}{R}w\right] \tag{7.10}$$

$$N_\theta = K\left[\frac{1}{R}\frac{\partial v_o}{\partial \theta} + \frac{w}{R} + v\frac{\partial u_o}{\partial x}\right] \tag{7.11}$$

$$N_{x\theta} = N_{\theta x} = \frac{1-\nu}{2} K \left[\frac{1}{R} \frac{\partial u_0}{\partial \theta} + \frac{\partial v_0}{\partial x} \right] \tag{7.12}$$

$$M_x = D \left[\frac{\partial \beta_x}{\partial x} + \frac{\nu}{R} \frac{\partial \beta_\theta}{\partial \theta} \right] \tag{7.13}$$

$$M_\theta = D \left[\frac{1}{R} \frac{\partial \beta_\theta}{\partial \theta} + \nu \frac{\partial \beta_x}{\partial x} \right] \tag{7.14}$$

$$M_{x\theta} = M_{\theta x} = \frac{1-\nu}{2} D \left[\frac{\partial \beta_\theta}{\partial x} + \frac{1}{R} \frac{\partial \beta_x}{\partial \theta} \right] \tag{7.15}$$

where

$$\begin{Bmatrix} N_x \\ N_0 \\ N_{x\theta} \\ Q_x \\ Q_\theta \end{Bmatrix} = \int_{-h/2}^{h/2} \begin{Bmatrix} \sigma_x \\ \sigma_\theta \\ \sigma_{x\theta} \\ \sigma_{xz} \\ \sigma_{\theta z} \end{Bmatrix} dz, \qquad \begin{Bmatrix} M_x \\ M_\theta \\ M_{x\theta} \end{Bmatrix} = \int_{-h/2}^{h/2} \begin{Bmatrix} \sigma_x \\ \sigma_\theta \\ \sigma_{x\theta} \end{Bmatrix} z \, dz$$

and

$$q_x = \sigma_{zx}(h/2) - \sigma_{zx}(-h/2) \equiv \tau_{1x} - \tau_{2x}$$

$$q_\theta = \sigma_{z\theta}(h/2) - \sigma_{z\theta}(-h/2) \equiv \tau_{1\theta} - \tau_{2\theta}$$

$$m_x = (h/2)[\sigma_{zx}(h/2) + \sigma_{zx}(-h/2)] \equiv (h/2)[\tau_{1x} + \tau_{2x}]$$

$$m_\theta = (h/2)[\sigma_{z\theta}(h/2) + \sigma_{z\theta}(-h/2)] \equiv (h/2)[\tau_{1\theta} + \tau_{2\theta}].$$

The above expressions for stress resultants, stress couples, and surface shear stresses are completely analogous to those for plates in Chapter 1.

The substitutions of Equations (7.8) and (7.9) into Equations (7.13) through (7.15) gives the stress couples in terms of the displacements u_o, v_o, and w. For simplicity, we let $R\theta \equiv s$, the arc length in the circumferential direction:

$$M_x = -D \left[\frac{\partial^2 w}{\partial x^2} + \nu \frac{\partial^2 w}{\partial s^2} - \frac{\nu}{R} \frac{\partial v_0}{\partial s} \right] \tag{7.16}$$

$$M_s = -D\left[\frac{\partial^2 w}{\partial s^2} - \frac{1}{R}\frac{\partial v_0}{\partial s} + v\frac{\partial^2 w}{\partial x^2}\right] \tag{7.17}$$

$$M_{xs} = M_{sx} = -\frac{1-v}{2}D\left[2\frac{\partial^2 w}{\partial x\partial s} - \frac{1}{R}\frac{\partial v_0}{\partial x}\right] \tag{7.18}$$

For lucidity, in what follows we shall drop the terms involving the surface shears q_x, q_s, m_x, m_s. Substituting Equations (7.16) through (7.18) into Equations (7.6) and (7.7) provides the shear resultants in terms of the displacements:

$$Q_x = -D\left[\frac{\partial}{\partial x}(\nabla^2 w) - \frac{1+v}{2R}\frac{\partial^2 v_0}{\partial x\partial s}\right] \tag{7.19}$$

$$Q_s = -D\left[\frac{\partial}{\partial s}(\nabla^2 w) - \frac{1-v}{2R}\frac{\partial^2 v_0}{\partial x^2} - \frac{1}{R}\frac{\partial^2 v_0}{\partial s^2}\right] \tag{7.20}$$

where $\qquad \nabla^2 \equiv \dfrac{\partial^2}{\partial x^2} + \dfrac{\partial^2}{\partial s^2}$

Substitution of Equations (7.10) through (7.20) into the force equilibrium equations (7.3) through (7.5) provides three simultaneous equations in terms of u, v, and w, which are the final governing equations to solve.

$$\frac{\partial^2 u_0}{\partial x^2} + \frac{1-v}{2}\frac{\partial^2 u_0}{\partial s^2} + \frac{1+v}{2}\frac{\partial^2 v_0}{\partial x\partial s} + \frac{v}{R}\frac{\partial w}{\partial x} = 0 \tag{7.21}$$

$$\left[\frac{1-v}{2}\frac{\partial^2 v_0}{\partial x^2} + \frac{\partial^2 v_0}{\partial s^2}\right] + \frac{1}{R}\frac{\partial w}{\partial s} + \frac{1+v}{2}\frac{\partial^2 u_0}{\partial x\partial s} - k^2 R\frac{\partial}{\partial s}(\nabla^2 w) = 0 \tag{7.22}$$

$$\nabla^4 w - \frac{1}{R}\frac{\partial}{\partial s}(\nabla^2 v_0) + \frac{1}{k^2}\left[\frac{1}{R^3}\frac{\partial v_0}{\partial s} + \frac{1}{R^4}w + \frac{v}{R^3}\frac{\partial u_0}{\partial x}\right] = \frac{p(x,s)}{D} \tag{7.23}$$

where $\qquad k^2 = h^2/12R^2$.

In Equations (7.21) through (7.23) Love's first approximation, given in Equation (7.2), is utilized.

These governing equations form an eighth-order system, which results in four boundary conditions on each edge. The application of variational principles (see Chapter 6) yields the following natural boundary conditions:

For an edge with x = constant:
Either u_0 prescribed or $N_x = 0$.
Either β_x prescribed or $M_x = 0$.
Either v_0 prescribed or $\bar{N}_{x\theta} = N_{x\theta} + M_{x\theta}/R = 0$.
Either w prescribed or $V_x = Q_x + \partial M_{x\theta}/\partial S = 0$.
For an edge with θ = constant:
Either v_0 prescribed or $N_\theta = 0$.
Either β_θ prescribed or $M_\theta = 0$.
Either u_0 prescribed or $\bar{N}_{\theta x} = \bar{N}_{x\theta} = 0$.
Either w prescribed or $V_\theta = Q_\theta + \partial M_{x\theta}/\partial x = 0$.

The quantities $\bar{N}_{x\theta}$ are "effective" in-plane forces on the edges of the shell. V_x and V_θ are "effective" transverse shear forces analogous to those discussed in Chapter 1 for a plate. These quantities are used because only four boundary conditions are obtained from the solution of the governing differential equations. Yet from physical reasoning, on a free x = constant edge the following boundary conditions must be satisfied: $N_x = N_{xs} = Q_x = M_x = M_{xs} = 0$. There are five of them, so according to the reasoning of Kirchoff, the shear forces and twisting moments are combined. In shell theories that retain transverse shear deformation and transverse normal stress, the system is tenth order, and no contraction of the boundary conditions is necessary.

For future reference, these effective boundary conditions are explicitly written in terms of the displacements:

$$\bar{N}_{xs} = \frac{1-\nu}{2}\left[K\left(\frac{\partial u_o}{\partial s} + \frac{\partial v_o}{\partial x}\right) - \frac{D}{R}\left(2\frac{\partial^2 w}{\partial x \partial s} - \frac{1}{R}\frac{\partial v_o}{\partial x}\right)\right]$$

(for an x = constant edge)

$$\bar{N}_{xs} = \frac{1-\nu}{2} K\left[\frac{\partial u_o}{\partial s} + \frac{\partial v_o}{\partial x}\right] \text{ (for a } \theta \text{ = constant edge)}$$

$$V_x = -D \left[\frac{\partial^3 v_o}{\partial x^3} + (2-\nu) \frac{\partial^3 w}{\partial x \partial s^2} - \frac{1}{R} \frac{\partial^2 v_o}{\partial x \partial s} \right]$$

$$V_\theta = -D \left[\frac{\partial^3 w}{\partial s^3} + (2-\nu) \frac{\partial^3 w}{\partial x^2 \partial s} - \frac{1-\nu}{\rho} \frac{\partial^2 v_o}{\partial x^2} - \frac{1}{R} \frac{\partial^2 v_o}{\partial s^2} \right]$$

It should be noted that if one first puts all the foregoing equations in terms of x and $s(=R\theta)$, and then sets R equal to infinity in its remaining occurrences, then the equations reduce to those of a flat rectangular plate of coordinates x and s, as in Chapter 1.

7.2. CIRCULAR CYLINDRICAL SHELLS UNDER AXIALLY SYMMETRIC LOADS

When the loads on a circular cylindrical shell are axially symmetric, then from symmetry in the circumferential direction it is seen that $v_0 = 0$, and $\partial/\partial\theta = 0$. It follows from Equations (7.7), (7.9), (7.12), and (7.15) that $Q_\theta = \beta_\theta = N_{x\theta} = M_{x\theta} = 0$. The resulting governing differential equations are therefore (here surface shear stresses have been omitted purely for simplicity; it is very simple to include them):

$$\frac{dN_x}{dx} = 0 \tag{7.24}$$

$$\frac{dQ_x}{dx} - \frac{N_\theta}{R} + p(x) = 0 \tag{7.25}$$

$$\frac{dM_x}{dx} - Q_x = 0 \tag{7.26}$$

$$\beta_x + \frac{dw}{dx} = 0 \tag{7.27}$$

$$N_x = K \left[\frac{du_0}{dx} + \frac{\nu}{R} w \right] \tag{7.28}$$

$$N_\theta = K \left[\nu \frac{du_0}{dx} + \frac{w}{R} \right] = \nu N_x + \frac{Ehw}{R} \tag{7.29}$$

$$M_x = -D\frac{d^2w}{dx^2} \tag{7.30}$$

$$M_\theta = -Dv\frac{d^2w}{dx^2} = vM_x \tag{7.31}$$

$$Q_x = -D\frac{d^3w}{dx^3} = V_x \tag{7.32}$$

It is seen from Equation (7.24) that N_x is constant everywhere in the shell and is uniquely determined by the boundary condition.

The governing equations in term of displacements, (7.21) through (7.23), reduce to two for the axially symmetric case, namely,

$$\frac{d^2u_0}{dx^2} + \frac{v}{R}\frac{dw}{dx} = 0 \tag{7.33}$$

$$\frac{d^4w}{dx^4} + \frac{1}{k^2R^4}w + \frac{v}{k^2R^3}\frac{du_0}{dx} = \frac{p(x)}{D} \tag{7.34}$$

Solving Equation (7.28) for du/dx, we can write Equation (7.34)

$$\frac{d^4w}{dx^4} + \frac{(1-v^2)}{k^2R^4}w = \frac{1}{D}\left[p - \frac{vN_x}{R}\right] \tag{7.35}$$

Substituting in the expression for k^2, we can write Equation (7.35) finally as

$$\frac{d^4w}{dx^4} + 4\varepsilon^4w = \frac{1}{D}\left[p - \frac{vN_x}{R}\right] \tag{7.36}$$

where $$\varepsilon^4 = \frac{3(1-v^2)}{h^2R^2} \tag{7.37}$$

The form of the governing equation (7.36) is desirable, as it is uncoupled from the other governing equation (7.33). N_x is a constant determined by boundary conditions. In fact, it is seen clearly that the effect of an axial in-plane force is the same as that of an equivalent lateral pressure as far as the lateral displacement w is concerned.

It should also be noted that the governing differential equation for the lateral deflection of a circular cylindrical shell has the same form as for that of a beam on an elastic foundation; it would be identical if D were replaced by EI, and $4\varepsilon^4 D$ by k, the foundation modulus. Thus one may use one's physical intuition as well as the known solutions for beams on elastic foundations in considering these shells.

By standard methods, the roots of the fourth-order equation (7.36) are determined to be $\pm \varepsilon(1 \pm i)$. Thus the general solution can be written in the form

$$w(x) = Ae^{-\varepsilon x}\cos \varepsilon x + Be^{-\varepsilon x}\sin \varepsilon x + Ce^{\varepsilon x}\cos \varepsilon x$$

$$+ Ee^{\varepsilon x}\sin \varepsilon x + w_p(x) \tag{7.38}$$

where A, B, C, and E are constants of integration determined by the boundary conditions, and $w_p(x)$ is the particular integral. The in-plane displacement u can be determined by one integration of Equation (7.28):

$$u_0(x) = \frac{N_x x}{K} - \frac{\nu}{R}\int w\,dx + F \tag{7.39}$$

where F is a constant of integration.

It is seen that for the case of circular cylindrical shells under axially symmetric loads there are six boundary conditions. Four deal with specifications of the lateral deflection, slope, stress couple, or shear resultant (w or its derivatives); the fifth is N_x, the in-plane stress resultant, which is determined at the outset by external equilibrium; and the sixth, F is determined by the specification of the in-plane displacement at the axis.

Before proceeding with some solutions, a sketch of the shell showing the positive directions of displacements and loads is needed. It is presented in Figure 7.1.

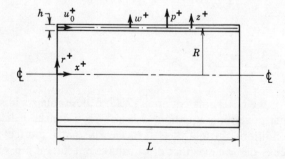

Fig. 7.1. Circular cylindrical shell-geometry, displacements, and coordinates.

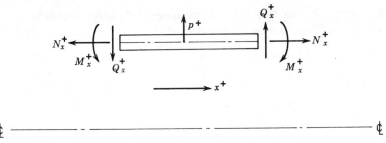

Fig. 7.2.   Circular cylindrical shell: stress resultants and couples.

The positive directions of stress resultants and couples are given in Figure 7.2.

7.3.   EDGE-LOAD SOLUTIONS

In the following, only the solutions for the lateral deflections are explicitly determined. The in-plane displacement u_0 can be subsequently determined easily from Equation (7.39).

7.3.1.   A Semi-infinite Shell $(0 \leqslant x \leqslant \infty)$ **Subjected to an Edge Moment** $M_x = M_0$ **at** $x = 0$

Since in this case (see Sketch 7.3) $p(x) = Nx = 0$, only the homogeneous portion of the general solution, Equation (7.38), is needed. The boundary conditions at $x = 0$ are

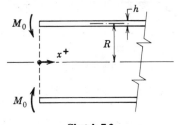

Sketch 7.3

$$M_x(0) = M_0 = -D \frac{d^2w(0)}{dx^2} \tag{7.40}$$

$$Q_x(0) = 0 = -D \frac{d^3w(0)}{dx^3} \tag{7.41}$$

Since we are dealing with small displacements (using linear theory), for w to remain finite as $x \to \infty$ it is required that $C = E = 0$. Hence we have

$$w(x) = Ae^{-\varepsilon x}\cos \varepsilon x + Be^{-\varepsilon x}\sin \varepsilon x \qquad (7.42)$$

Substituting Equation (7.42) into Equations (7.40) and (7.41), we obtain

$$w''(0) = -2\varepsilon^2 B = -\frac{M_0}{D}$$

$$w'''(0) = 2\varepsilon^3(A + B) = 0$$

where primes denote differentiation with respect to x.
Thus $B = -A = M_0/2\varepsilon^2 D$, and the solution is

$$w(x) = \frac{M_0}{2\varepsilon^2 D}e^{-\varepsilon x}(\sin \varepsilon x - \cos \varepsilon x) \qquad (7.43)$$

Of course, knowing $w(x)$, one can obtain M_x, Q_x, u_0 everywhere.

7.3.2. A Semi-infinite Shell ($0 \leqslant x \leqslant \infty$) Subjected to an Edge Shear $Q_x = Q_0$ at $x = 0$

Here (see Sketch 7.4) the bounary conditions are

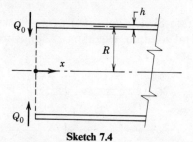

Sketch 7.4

$$M_x(0) = 0 = -Dw'' \qquad (7.44)$$

$$Q_x(0) = Q_0 = -Dw''' \qquad (7.45)$$

Again it is required that $C = E = 0$, and the solution is given by Equation (7.42). Substituting Equation (7.42) into Equations (7.44) and (7.45) results in

$$2\varepsilon^2 B = 0$$

$$2\varepsilon^3(A + B) = -\frac{Q_0}{D}$$

The solution is therefore

$$w(x) = -\frac{Q_0}{2\varepsilon^3 D} e^{-\varepsilon x} \cos \varepsilon x. \qquad (7.46)$$

7.3.3. Edge-Load Solutions as the Homogeneous Solution

It is seen that the solutions of Equations (7.43) and (7.46) exhibit the same form: a constant times an oscillating (trigonometric) factor and a factor that exhibits exponential decay away from the edge of the shell. This decay in the lateral deflecton due to a stress couple or a transverse shear resultant is characteristic of shells in general, and is one of the most important features of shell behavior. Since the slope, bending moment, and shear resultant away from the edge are all proportional to the derivatives of the lateral deflection, each of these also decays away from the edge where the edge load is acting. The region of decay is called the *bending boundary layer*, and it is seen that bending and shear stresses due to the edge load occur only in this layer.

Now the lateral deflection, slope, bending moment, and transverse shear resultant all decay as $e^{-\varepsilon x}$, where $\varepsilon = [3(1-\nu^2)]^{1/4}/\sqrt{Rh}$. Hence $x/\sqrt{Rh}$ is a fundamentally important parameter with regard to shell behavior. It is seen, for example, that $x/\sqrt{Rh} \geqslant 4$ occurs when $\varepsilon x \geqslant 5.15$ when $\nu = 0.3$. This then results in $e^{-\varepsilon x} \leqslant 0.006$, and therefore the lateral deflection, slope, moment, and shear for $x/\sqrt{Rh} \geqslant 4$ are negligibly small. Therefore the length L_B of the bending boundary layer is taken to be $L_B = 4\sqrt{Rh}$.*

This suggests a very useful solution technique for shell problems. Consider a finite-length shell subjected to axially symmetric loading and a set of stated boundary conditions. Instead of satisfying the boundary conditions directly by obtaining values of A, B, C, and E in Equation (7.38), one can use the edge load solutions as the homogeneous solution and satisfy the boundary conditions by determining the values necessary for the edge stress couples and edge shear resultants. The advantage of this method is that the effects of the particular boundary conditions on w and its derivatives become negligible at a distance L_B away from the edge. Further away from the edge, only the particular solution will contribute to the lateral deflection, slope, bending moments, and transverse shear. Hence if

---

*It can be shown that this can be generalized to any shell of revolution under axially symmetric edge load by defining $L_B = 4\sqrt{R_\theta h}$, where R_θ is the circumferential radius of curvature at the edge.

the length of the shell is $L \geqslant L_B$, the boundary conditions involving w and its derivatives at one end of the shell are uncoupled from those at the other end. Mathematically, this means that for a shell of $L \geqslant L_B$, instead of solving a 4×4 matrix* to obtain the boundary conditions, one solves two 2×2 matrices.

Using the edge load form of the solution, we may write the homogeneous solution for a shell of length L as

$$w(x) = \frac{M_0}{2\varepsilon^2 D} e^{-\varepsilon x} (\sin \varepsilon x - \cos \varepsilon x) - \frac{Q_0}{2\varepsilon^3 D} e^{-\varepsilon x} \cos \varepsilon x$$

$$+ \frac{M_L}{2\varepsilon^2 D} e^{-\varepsilon(L-x)} [\sin \varepsilon (L-x) - \cos \varepsilon (L-x)] \qquad (7.47)$$

$$+ \frac{Q_L}{2\varepsilon^3 D} e^{-\varepsilon(L-x)} \cos \varepsilon (L-x)$$

where the edge loads are considered positive as shown in Figure 7.3 below:

It should be noted from Equation (7.39) that not all of the terms in the $u_0(x)$ equation decay away from the edges—only the second term as written. Of the others, one increases monotonically in x, and the other is a constant. At any rate, outside the bending boundary layer at each edge, the expression for u_0 is simplified.

Even when the shell is so short that $L < L_B$, in which case there is no separation of the boundary conditions, there is no practical advantage in

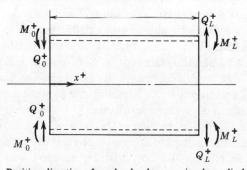

Fig. 7.3.   Positive directions for edge loads on a circular cylindrical shell.

---

*Actually one starts with a 6×6 matrix for a general shell of revolution under axially symmetric load, but for cylindrical shells, N_x is found by a trivial force balance, and the boundary constant F in the $u_0(x)$ equation is always found subsequent to finding the four boundary constants involving w and its derivatives.

using the form of the homogeneous solution given by Equation (7.38) rather than that in Equation (7.47).

7.4 A GENERAL SOLUTION FOR CYLINDRICAL SHELLS UNDER AXIALLY SYMMETRIC LOADS

For reference in solving problems of this kind, all equations needed are catalogued below (see Figure 7.3). They are restricted to cases where $d^4p(x)/dx^4 = 0$. Since this is almost always true in practice, the solutions presented below are fairly general.

$$w(x) = \frac{M_0}{2\varepsilon^2 D}e^{-\varepsilon x}(\sin\varepsilon x - \cos\varepsilon x) - \frac{Q_0}{2\varepsilon^3 D}e^{-\varepsilon x}\cos\varepsilon x$$

$$+ \frac{M_L}{2\varepsilon^2 D}e^{-\varepsilon(L-x)}[\sin\varepsilon(L-x) - \cos\varepsilon(L-x)]$$

$$+ \frac{Q_L}{2\varepsilon^3 D}e^{-\varepsilon(L-x)}\cos\varepsilon(L-x) + \frac{1}{4\varepsilon^4 D}\left[p(x) - \frac{\nu N_x}{R}\right] \qquad (7.48)$$

where $\quad \varepsilon = [3(1-\nu^2)]^{1/4}/\sqrt{Rh}$

$$w'(x) = \frac{dw}{dx} = \frac{M_0}{\varepsilon D}e^{-\varepsilon x}\cos\varepsilon x + \frac{Q_0}{2\varepsilon^2 D}e^{-\varepsilon x}(\sin\varepsilon x + \cos\varepsilon x)$$

$$- \frac{M_L}{\varepsilon D}e^{-\varepsilon(L-x)}\cos\varepsilon(L-x)$$

$$+ \frac{Q_L}{2\varepsilon^2 D}e^{-\varepsilon(L-x)}[\sin\varepsilon(L-x) + \cos\varepsilon(L-x)] + \frac{1}{4\varepsilon^4 D}p'(x) \qquad (7.49)$$

$$M_x(x) = -Dw''(x) = M_0 e^{-\varepsilon x}(\sin\varepsilon x + \cos\varepsilon x) + \frac{Q_0}{\varepsilon}e^{-\varepsilon x}\sin\varepsilon x$$

$$+ M_L e^{-\varepsilon(L-x)}[\sin\varepsilon(L-x) + \cos\varepsilon(L-x)]$$

$$- \frac{Q_L}{\varepsilon}e^{-\varepsilon(L-x)}\sin\varepsilon(L-x) - \frac{1}{4\varepsilon^4}p''(x) \qquad (7.50)$$

$$Q_x = -Dw'''(x) = -2M_0\varepsilon e^{-\varepsilon x}\sin\varepsilon x + Q_0 e^{-\varepsilon x}(\cos\varepsilon x - \sin\varepsilon x)$$

$$+2M_L\varepsilon e^{-\varepsilon(L-x)}\sin\varepsilon(L-x)$$

$$-Q_L e^{-\varepsilon(L-x)}[-\cos\varepsilon(L-x)+\sin\varepsilon(L-x)]-\frac{1}{4\varepsilon^4}p'''(x) \qquad (7.51)$$

$$u_0(x) = \left[\frac{1}{K}+\frac{\nu^2}{4R^2\varepsilon^4 D}\right]N_x x - \frac{\nu}{R}\left\{-\frac{M_0}{2\varepsilon^3 D}e^{-\varepsilon x}\sin\varepsilon x\right.$$

$$+\frac{Q_0}{4\varepsilon^4 D}e^{-\varepsilon x}(\cos\varepsilon x - \sin\varepsilon x)+\frac{M_L}{2\varepsilon^3 D}e^{-\varepsilon(L-x)}\sin\varepsilon(L-x)$$

$$\left.+\frac{Q_L}{4\varepsilon^4 D}e^{-\varepsilon(L-x)}[\cos\varepsilon(L-x)-\sin\varepsilon(L-x)]\right\}$$

$$-\frac{\nu}{4R\varepsilon^4 D}\int p(x)\,dx + F \qquad (7.52)$$

$$N_x = \text{constant} \qquad (7.53)$$

$$N_\theta(x) = \nu N_x + \frac{Ehw(x)}{R} \qquad (7.54)$$

$$M_\theta(x) = \nu M_x(x) \qquad (7.55)$$

$$\sigma_x = \frac{N_x}{h}+\frac{M_x z}{h^3/12} \qquad (7.56)$$

$$\sigma_\theta = \frac{N_\theta}{h}+\frac{M_\theta z}{h^3/12} = \nu\sigma_x + \frac{Ew(x)}{R} \qquad (7.57)$$

$$\sigma_{xz} = \frac{3Q_x}{2h}\left[1-\left(\frac{z}{h/2}\right)^2\right] \qquad (7.58)$$

The edge-load solutions for a conical shell are provided by Vinson,[1] and those for hemispherical shells are provided by ASME.[2] Since these are often connected to cylindrical shells in many actual structures, their use is frequent.

Problems involving cylindrical shells of composite materials are also treated by Vinson and Chou.[15]

7.5 SAMPLE SOLUTIONS

7.5.1 Effects of Simple and Clamped Supports

Consider the circular cylindrical shell shown in sketch 7.5 below. The end of the shell $x=0$ is simply supported, the end $x=L$ is clamped. The plate ends of the shell are assumed rigid. The internal pressure is p_0, and $\nu = 0.3$. The following information is desired:

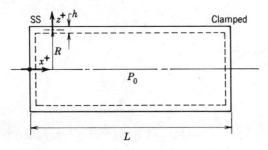

Sketch 7.5

1. What are the magnitude and the exact location of the maximum stress in the bending boundary layer at the simply supported end?

2. What are they near the clamped end?

3. What is the magnitude of the maximum stress outside the bending boundary layers, say at $x = L/2$?

4. If the maximum-principal-stress failure theory is applicable, would the shell be structurally sound if in the design the thickness had been determined by membrane shell theory? (Membrance shell theory neglects all bending effects; see Section 7.10.) From external-axial-force equilibrium, $N_x = p_0 R/2$. The boundary conditions at $x=0$ are $w(0)=0$ and $M_x(0)=0$. From Equations (7.48) and (7.50), the boundary conditions are

$$w(0) = -\frac{M_0}{2\varepsilon^2 D} - \frac{Q_0}{2\varepsilon^3 D} + \frac{1}{4\varepsilon^4 D} p_0 \left(1 - \frac{\nu}{2}\right)$$

$$M_x(0) = M_0 = 0 \tag{7.59}$$

Hence

$$Q_0 = \frac{p_0}{2\varepsilon}\left(1 - \frac{\nu}{2}\right) \tag{7.60}$$

To determine the location of the maximum value of σ_x, the location of the maximum of M_x will suffice since N_x is a constant. Since M_x is zero at $x=0$ and again for $x \geqslant L_B$, the extremum values lie somewhere in the bending boundary layer. They occur at values of x such that $dM_x/dx = 0$. Since $dM_x/dx = Q_x$, the extrema occur at $Q_x = 0$. We now make use of Equation (7.59), since p_0 is constant and the shell is long, the effects of M_L and Q_L are negligible. Then Equation (7.51) becomes $Q_x = (p_0/2)(1-\nu/2)$ $e^{-\varepsilon x}(\cos\varepsilon x - \sin\varepsilon x) = 0$. For this condition to exist, we must have $\cos\varepsilon x = \sin\varepsilon x$, or $\varepsilon x = \pi/4, 5\pi/4$, etc. Since there is an exponential decay with increasing x, the largest extreme value—the maximum—occurs at $\varepsilon x = \pi/4$. Hence

$$M_{x\max} = M_x\left(\frac{\pi}{4\varepsilon}\right) = p_0\left(1 - \frac{\nu}{2}\right)\frac{\sqrt{2}}{4\varepsilon^2}e^{-\pi/4}.$$

From Equation (7.56),

$$\sigma_{x\max} = \frac{N_x}{h} \pm \frac{6M_{x\max}}{h^2}$$

$$= \frac{p_0 R}{2h} \pm 0.498\frac{p_0 R}{h} \qquad \text{for } \nu = 0.3$$

$$\sigma_{x\max} = \sigma_x\left(\frac{\pi}{4\varepsilon}, +\frac{h}{2}\right) = 0.998\frac{p_0 R}{h} \tag{7.61}$$

From Equations (7.59), (7.60), (7.48), and (7.50),

$$w(x) = \frac{p_0(1-\nu/2)}{4\varepsilon^4 D}[1 - e^{-\varepsilon x}\cos\varepsilon x] \qquad \text{for } x \leqslant L_B \tag{7.62}$$

$$M(x) = \frac{p_0(1-\nu/2)}{2\varepsilon^2}e^{-\varepsilon x}\sin\varepsilon x \qquad \text{for } x \leqslant L_B \tag{7.63}$$

Therefore, from Equations (7.57), (7.62), and (7.63),

$$\sigma_\theta = \frac{p_0 R}{h} \pm \frac{3\nu(1-\nu/2)Rp_0 e^{-\varepsilon x}\sin\varepsilon x}{h[3(1-\nu^2)]^{1/2}} - \frac{p_0(1-\nu/2)Re^{-\varepsilon x}\cos\varepsilon x}{h}$$

$$\text{for } z = \pm h/2 \tag{7.64}$$

For $\nu = 0.3$, this reduces to

$$\sigma_\theta = \frac{p_0 c}{h}\left\{1 \pm 0.464e^{-\varepsilon x}\sin\varepsilon x - 0.85e^{-\varepsilon x}\cos\varepsilon x\right\} \qquad \text{for } x \leqslant L_B, z = \pm\frac{h}{2}$$

Extreme values occur for $\partial\sigma_\theta/\partial_x = 0$, which results in the requirement that

$$\pm 0.464(-\sin \varepsilon x + \cos \varepsilon x) + 0.85(\sin \varepsilon x + \cos \varepsilon x) = 0$$

For the positive sign this occurs at $\varepsilon x = 1.875$; for the negative, at $\varepsilon x = 2.845$. Of these two values, σ_θ is greater for the former. The maximum value of σ_θ in the range $x \leqslant L_B$ is therefore

$$\sigma_{\theta \max} = \sigma_\theta \left(\frac{1.875}{\varepsilon}, + \frac{h}{2} \right) = 1.1072 \frac{p_0 R}{h} \qquad \text{for } \nu = 0.3 \qquad (7.65)$$

At the clamped end the boundary conditions are $w(L) = w'(L) = 0$. From Equations (7.48) and (7.49), and making use of the fact that the shell is long $(L > 4\sqrt{Rh}\,)$, we have

$$w(L) = 0 = -\frac{M_L}{2\varepsilon^2 D} + \frac{Q_L}{2\varepsilon^3 D} + \frac{p_0}{4\varepsilon^4 D}\left(1 - \frac{\nu}{2}\right) = 0$$

$$w'(L) = 0 = -\frac{M_L}{\varepsilon D} + \frac{Q_L}{2\varepsilon^2 D} = 0$$

Hence

$$M_L = -\frac{p_0(1 - \nu/2)}{2\varepsilon^2} \qquad (7.66)$$

$$Q_L = -\frac{p_0(1 - \nu/2)}{\varepsilon} \qquad (7.67)$$

It can be shown, and is physically obvious, that at the clamped end, $M_{x\max} = M(L) = M_L$. Hence at $x = L$,

$$\sigma_x = \frac{N_x}{h} + \frac{M_L z}{h^3/12} = \frac{p_0 R}{2h} - \frac{p_0(1 - \nu/2)z}{2\varepsilon^2 h^3/12}$$

$$\sigma_{x\max} = \sigma_x \left(L, -\frac{h}{2} \right) = 2.04 \frac{p_0 R}{h} \qquad \text{for } \nu = 0.3 \qquad (7.68)$$

However, $\sigma_{\theta \max}$ occurs away from the end of the shell. Analogously to the procedures used at the other end, it is found that

$$\sigma_{\theta \max} = \sigma_\theta \left(L - \frac{2.65}{\varepsilon}, + \frac{h}{2} \right) = 1.069 \frac{p_0 R}{h} \qquad (7.69)$$

At $x = L/2$, which is outside either bending boundary layer, it is seen from Equation (7.50) that $M_x = 0$; hence

$$\sigma_x = \frac{N_x}{h} = \frac{p_0 R}{2h} \tag{7.70}$$

which is the membrance solution. Likewise,

$$\sigma_\theta = \nu\sigma_x + \frac{Ew}{R} = \frac{p_0 R}{h} \tag{7.71}$$

which is also the membrane solution.

It is seen from Equation (7.65) that the maximum principal stress occurring in the boundary layer at the simply supported end is $1.1072 p_0 R/h$; correspondingly, from Equation (7.68), at the clamped end it is $2.04 p_0 R/h$. The maximum stress predicted by membrane theory is $1.0 p_0 R/h$. Hence stresses greater than membrane stresses occur in both boundary layers: 10% higher near the simply supported edge, and 104% higher at the clamped edge. Thus this shell, if designed on a basis of membrane shell theory, would be woefully inadequate.

In the above, we have determined the location of the maximum axial stress and the maximum circumferential stress in the bending boundary layer at each end of the shell. It should be remembered that everywhere there is at least a biaxial stress state. Hence, if we are dealing with a material that imposes a yield or fracture criterion (such as a maximum distortion energy, maximum shear stress, or any of several others), then that criterion must be used to find the location of the maximum value of the equivalent uniaxial stress state. Quite often a very simple digital-computer routine can be employed to do the arithmetic, using the analytical solution, to determine the location and magnitude of the maximum stress.

7.5.2 Supports by Elastic Rings

Consider the long shell described in the previous subsection, but with each shell end supported by an elastic ring that has negligible rigidity against out of plane rotation. In that case $M(0) = M(L) = M_0 = M_L = 0$. From Equation (7.48),

$$w(x) = -\frac{Q_0}{2\varepsilon^3 D} e^{-\varepsilon x} \cos\varepsilon x + \frac{Q_L}{2\varepsilon^3 D} e^{-\varepsilon(L-x)} \cos\varepsilon(L-x) + \frac{p_0(1-\nu/2)}{4\varepsilon^4 D}$$

$$\tag{7.72}$$

Force equilibrium on a segment of the ring requires the following (where the subscript r refers to the ring):

$$\sigma_{\theta r} = -\frac{RQ_0}{A_r} = +\frac{RQ_L}{A_r} \tag{7.73}$$

Here $A_r =$ ring cross-sectional area. From ring theory

$$\varepsilon_{\theta r} = \frac{w_r}{R} = \frac{\sigma_{\theta r}}{E_r} = -\frac{RQ_0}{A_r E_r} = \frac{RQ_L}{A_r E_r} \tag{7.74}$$

For the ring to support the shell, it is required that

$$w(0) = w_R \quad \text{and} \quad w(L) = w_R \tag{7.75}$$

Hence the remaining boundary conditions are

$$-\frac{Q_0 R^2}{A_R E_R} = -\frac{Q_0}{2\varepsilon^3 D} + \frac{p_0(1-\nu/2)}{4\varepsilon^4 D} \tag{7.76}$$

$$\frac{Q_L R^2}{A_R E_R} = \frac{Q_L}{2\varepsilon^3 D} + \frac{p_0(1-\nu/2)}{4\varepsilon^4 D} \tag{7.77}$$

Solving for Q_0 and Q_L, it is seen that

$$w(x) = \frac{p_0(1-\nu/2)}{4\varepsilon^4 D}\left\{1 - \frac{1}{1 + 2\varepsilon^3 DR^2/E_R A_R}\left[e^{-\varepsilon x}\cos\varepsilon x\right.\right.$$
$$\left.\left. + e^{-\varepsilon(L-x)}\cos\varepsilon(L-x)\right]\right\} \tag{7.78}$$

From this solution all other quantities are obtained by use of the equations of Section 7.4.

Note that if the rings are infinitely stiff ($E_R = \infty$), the solution reduces to that for the shell on simple supports. Also note that outside the bending layer at each end, only the particular solution, which is the membrane solution, remains.

Also, if the ring did have significant stiffness against out of plane rotation, then the stress couple of the shell at each end could be related to the torsional stiffness of the ring, by an analogous argument.

7.5.3. An Infinite Shell $(-\infty \leqslant x \leqslant +\infty)$ Subjected to a Radial Line Load at $x=0$

In this case (see sketch 7.6), $p(x)=0$, $N_x=0$, and only the homogeneous solution is used. Since the shell and loading are symmetric with respect to $x=0$, we need only consider the half of the shell $0 \leqslant x \leqslant \infty$. From symmetry it is easily deduced that $Q_0 = -H/2$. The edge moment M_0 is then used to enforce the boundary condition that the slope at $x=0$ must be zero. Thus, combining Equations (7.48) and (7.49), we obtain

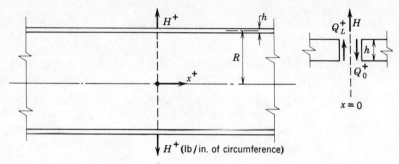

$$H^+ \text{ (lb / in. of circumference)}$$

Sketch 7.6

$$w(x) = \frac{M_0}{2\varepsilon^2 D} e^{-\varepsilon x} (\sin \varepsilon x - \cos \varepsilon x) - \frac{Q_0}{2\varepsilon^3 D} e^{-\varepsilon x} \cos \varepsilon x \qquad (7.79)$$

$$w'(x) = \frac{M_0}{\varepsilon D} e^{-\varepsilon x} \cos \varepsilon x + \frac{Q_0}{2\varepsilon^2 D} e^{-\varepsilon x} (\cos \varepsilon x + \sin \varepsilon x) \qquad (7.80)$$

and at $x=0$,

$$w'(0) = 0 = \frac{M_0}{\varepsilon D} + \frac{Q_0}{2\varepsilon^2 D} \qquad (7.81)$$

Since $Q_0 = -H/2$, we have $M_0 = H/4\varepsilon$.

The solution is then written as

$$w(x) = \frac{H}{8\varepsilon^3 D} e^{-\varepsilon x} (\sin \varepsilon x + \cos \varepsilon x) \qquad x \geqslant 0 \qquad (7.82)$$

As mentioned previously, the lateral deflection is symmetric with respect to $x=0$.

Again the decay $e^{-\varepsilon x}$ is present, just as in the case of edge loads. This result can be generalized. In a region of dimension $4\sqrt{Rh}$ about any edge, structural discontinuity or load discontinuity, there will exist bending stresses; outside of this region only membrane stresses and displacements will exist. This is true for any shell of revolution if R_θ, the circumferential radius of curvature, is used in determining the length of the bending boundary layer.

7.6. CIRCULAR CYLINDRICAL SHELLS UNDER ASYMMETRIC LOADS

The full set of equations for circular cylindrical shells under an asymmetric load is given by Equations (7.3) through (7.15). The applied loads are $p(x,\theta)$ and

$$\tau_{1x} = \sigma_{rx}\left(+\frac{h}{2} \right)$$

$$\tau_{2x} = \sigma_{rx}\left(-\frac{h}{2} \right)$$

$$\tau_{1\theta} = \sigma_{r\theta}\left(+\frac{h}{2} \right)$$ (7.83)

$$\tau_{2\theta} = \sigma_{r\theta}\left(-\frac{h}{2} \right)$$

The quantities defined in Equation (7.83) are *known* applied surface shear loadings for a single-layer shell, or for the outer surface of a multilayer shell. However, on the inner surfaces of a multilayer shell, such quantities are *unknown* and are included among the dependent variables for which solutions must be found.

For most asymmetric loads it is convenient to expand the applied loads into Fourier series:

$$f(x,\theta) = \sum_{n=0}^{\infty} f_n(x) \left\{ \begin{array}{c} \cos n\theta \\ \sin n\theta \end{array} \right\}$$ (7.84)

where $f(x,\theta)$ is $p(x,\theta)$, τ_{1x}, τ_{2x}, $\tau_{1\theta}$, or $\tau_{2\theta}$.

Likewise, all dependent variables are expanded into Fourier series:

$$g(x,\theta) = \sum_{n=0}^{\infty} g_n(x) \left\{ \begin{array}{c} \cos n\theta \\ \sin n\theta \end{array} \right\}$$ (7.85)

where $g(x, \theta)$ can be w, u_0, v_0, M_x, M_θ, $M_{x\theta}$, N_x, N_θ, $N_{x\theta}$, Q_x, Q_θ, β_x, or β_θ.

Substituting Equations (7.84) and (7.85) into Equations (7.3) through (7.15) results in a complete set of ordinary differential equations in x. Obviously, proper substitution will result in three simultaneous differential equations in u_{0n}, v_{0n}, and w_n with constant coefficients, analogous to Equations (7.21) through (7.23).

The solution of these equations is straightforward. An eighth-order algebraic equation is obtained, from which the roots are found. Because of the complexity of the expressions for the constant coefficients, the roots are usually obtained after substituting numbers for geometrical and material parameters, rather than in algebraic generality. When obtaining the numerical roots, care must be exercised in retaining sufficient accuracy (significant figures) that subsequent differentiation of the displacements to find the stresses does not introduce significant errors. Also, for any other geometry, material, or load the roots must be obtained again.

An alternative to the foregoing is to utilize a simplified shell theory in which the roots are obtained in algebraic form. One such theory is known as shallow-shell theory.

7.7. SHALLOW-SHELL THEORY (DONNELL'S EQUATIONS)

Donnell[3] formulated his theory in 1933 in his study of the elastic stability of cylindrical shells. Since that time the approximations have been used extensively in stress and vibration analysis. The shallow-shell equations are simpler than the full set, and can be decoupled. Further, for cylindrical shells the roots can be obtained with algebraic generality.

The shallow-shell equations are accurate for thin shells except near a very localized loading.

Hoff, Kempner and Pohle[4] have systematically compared Donnell shallow-shell-theory results with those of the more complicated shell theory of Flügge. The results for $n = 1$ displayed the greatest difference, and it was only a few percent. For $n \gg 1$ Donnell-theory solutions accurately match those of Flügge.

Donnell-type equations, including transverse shear deformation, which incorporate the ε / R_θ terms, have been found to be accurate for thick shells subjected to line loads. For $R/h = 10$, the solution agrees very well with a three-dimensional elasticity solution.

To obtain the Donnell equations from the full set, the following two approximations are made. (*Note*: The following assumptions are made in transforming shell equations of any geometry to shallow-shell equations for that geometry, and are not limited to cylindrical shells.)

1. Use the moment-curvature relations for plates (i.e., neglect initial curvature).

2. Neglect the effect of the transverse shear force Q_θ on the balance of forces in the circumferential direction.

Employing these two assumptions, the general set of Equations (7.3) through (7.20) become (neglecting surface shear stresses):

$$\frac{\partial N_x}{\partial x} + \frac{\partial N_{x\theta}}{R\partial \theta} = 0 \tag{7.86}$$

$$\frac{\partial N_{x\theta}}{\partial x} + \frac{1}{R}\frac{\partial N_\theta}{\partial \theta} = 0* \tag{7.87}$$

$$\frac{\partial Q_x}{\partial x} + \frac{1}{R}\frac{\partial Q_\theta}{\partial \theta} - \frac{1}{R}N_\theta + p(x,\theta) = 0 \tag{7.88}$$

$$\frac{\partial M_x}{\partial x} + \frac{1}{R}\frac{\partial M_{x\theta}}{\partial \theta} - Q_x = 0 \tag{7.89}$$

$$\frac{\partial M_{x\theta}}{\partial x} + \frac{1}{R}\frac{\partial M_\theta}{\partial \theta} - Q_\theta = 0 \tag{7.90}$$

$$N_x = K\left[\frac{\partial u_0}{\partial x} + \frac{\nu}{R}\frac{\partial v_0}{\partial \theta} + \frac{\nu}{R}w\right] \tag{7.91}$$

$$N_\theta = K\left[\frac{1}{R}\frac{\partial v_0}{\partial \theta} + \nu\frac{\partial u_0}{\partial x} + \frac{w}{R}\right] \tag{7.92}$$

$$N_{x\theta} = N_{\theta x} = \left(\frac{1-\nu}{2}\right)K\left[\frac{1}{R}\frac{\partial u_0}{\partial \theta} + \frac{\partial v_0}{\partial x}\right] \tag{7.93}$$

$$M_x = -D\left[\frac{\partial^2 w}{\partial x^2} + \frac{\nu}{R^2}\frac{\partial^2 w}{\partial \theta^2}\right]^* \tag{7.94}$$

$$M_\theta = -D\left[\frac{1}{R^2}\frac{\partial^2 w}{\partial \theta^2} + \nu\frac{\partial^2 w}{\partial x^2}\right]^* \tag{7.95}$$

$$M_{x\theta} = M_{\theta x} = -\frac{1-\nu}{R}D\frac{\partial^2 w}{\partial x\partial \theta}^* \tag{7.96}$$

$$Qx = -D \frac{\partial}{\partial x} (\nabla^2 w) *$$ (7.97)

$$Q_\theta = -\frac{D}{R} \frac{\partial}{\partial \theta} (\nabla^2 w) *$$ (7.98)

The effective shear resultants associated with free edges become

$$V_x = -D \left[\frac{\partial^3 w}{\partial x^3} + \frac{2-\nu}{R^2} \frac{\partial^3 w}{\partial x \partial \theta^2} \right]^*$$ (7.99)

$$V_\theta = -D \left[\frac{1}{R^3} \frac{\partial^3 w}{\partial \theta^3} + \frac{2-\nu}{R} \frac{\partial^3 w}{\partial x^2 \partial \theta} \right]^*$$ (7.100)

In the above, an asterisk denotes equations that differ from those of the complete unsimplified set.

Proceeding as before in Section 7.2, we obtain three simultaneous force equilibrium equations in terms of the two midsurface displacements u_0 and v_0, and the lateral displacement w.

$$\frac{\partial^2 u_0}{\partial x^2} + \frac{1-\nu}{2} \frac{\partial^2 u_0}{\partial s^2} + \frac{1+\nu}{2} \frac{\partial^2 v_0}{\partial x \partial s} + \frac{\nu}{R} \frac{\partial w}{\partial x} = 0$$ (7.101)

$$\frac{1-\nu}{2} \frac{\partial^2 v_0}{\partial x^2} + \frac{\partial^2 v_0}{\partial s^2} + \frac{1+\nu}{2} \frac{\partial^2 u_0}{\partial x \partial s} + \frac{1}{R} \frac{\partial w}{\partial s} = 0$$ (7.102)

$$\nabla^4 w + \frac{12}{h^2 R} \left[\frac{\partial v_0}{\partial s} + \frac{w}{R} + \nu \frac{\partial u_0}{\partial x} \right] = \frac{p(x,s)}{D}$$ (7.103)

A comparison of these with Equations (7.21) through (7.23) provides a clear picture of what simplifications result from the shallow-shell assumptions. Manipulation of the three equations above results in the Donnell equations, shown below in their familiar form.

$$\nabla^4 u_o = -\frac{1}{R} \frac{\partial}{\partial x} \left[\nu \frac{\partial^2 w}{\partial x^2} - \frac{\partial^2 w}{\partial s^2} \right]$$ (7.104)

$$\nabla^4 v_o = -\frac{1}{R} \frac{\partial}{\partial s} \left[(2+\nu) \frac{\partial^2 w}{\partial x^2} + \frac{\partial^2 w}{\partial s^2} \right]$$ (7.105)

$$\nabla^8 w + 4\varepsilon^4 \frac{\partial^4 w}{\partial x^4} = \frac{1}{D} \nabla^4 p(x,s) \tag{7.106}$$

The last equation is uncoupled from the first two. Upon its solution, the first two are subsequently solved by substituting w into the right-hand sides of each.

If the circular cylindrical shell is complete in the circumferential direction ($0 \leqslant \theta \leqslant 2\pi$), one approach to the solution is to reduce the above to three ordinary differential equations in x, by using the form of the displacements u_0, v_0, and w given in Equation (7.85) and the form of the lateral load $p(x,\theta)$ given in Equation (7.84). Proceeding in this manner, one obtains the governing equations for the homogeneous solution as follows:

$$U_n^{\text{IV}} - \frac{2n^2}{R^2} U_n'' + \frac{n^4}{R^4} U_n = \frac{1}{R}\left[-\frac{n^2}{R^2} W_n' - \nu W_n''' \right] \tag{7.107}$$

$$V_n^{\text{IV}} - \frac{2n^2}{R^2} V_n'' + \frac{n^4}{R^4} V_n = -\frac{1}{R}\left[-\frac{(2+\nu)n}{R} W_n'' + \frac{n^3}{R^3} W_n \right] \tag{7.108}$$

$$W_n^{\text{VIII}} - \frac{4n^2}{R^2} W_n^{\text{VI}} + \frac{6n^4}{R^4} W_n^{\text{IV}} - \frac{4n^6}{R^6} W_n'' + \frac{n^8}{R^8} W_n + 4\varepsilon^4 W_n^{\text{IV}} = 0 \tag{7.109}$$

Assuming the homogeneous solution for W_n to be of the form

$$W_n = A_{jn} e^{\lambda_{jn} x} \tag{7.110}$$

its substitution into Equation (7.109) results in the following characteristic equation, which provides eight roots for each value of n.

$$\left[\lambda_{jn}^2 - \frac{n^2}{R^2} \right]^4 + 4\varepsilon^4 \lambda_{jn}^4 = 0 \qquad (j = 1,2,\ldots,8) \tag{7.111}$$

This can be written as

$$\lambda_{jn}^2 - \frac{n^2}{R^2} = \varepsilon \lambda_{jn} \begin{Bmatrix} 1+i \\ 1-i \\ -1+i \\ -1-i \end{Bmatrix} \tag{7.112}$$

It is seen that λ_{jn} must be complex. Hence if λ_{jn} is a root, its complex conjugate $\bar{\lambda}_{jn}$ must also be a root. Also, since Equation (7.109) contains only even powers of λ_{jn}, it follows that $-\lambda_{jn}$ and $-\bar{\lambda}_{jn}$ are also roots. Therefore, for each n, all eight roots are obtained if two independent roots are found. The following are taken arbitrarily from Equation (7.112) as the two independent equations.

$$\lambda_{1n}^2 - \frac{n^2}{R^2} = \varepsilon\lambda_{1n}(1+i) \tag{7.113}$$

$$\lambda_{2n}^2 - \frac{n^2}{R^2} = -\varepsilon\lambda_{2n}(1+i) \tag{7.114}$$

Solutions are easily obtained:

$$\lambda_{1n} = \frac{1+i}{2}\varepsilon + \frac{1}{2}\sqrt{(1+i)^2\varepsilon^2 + \frac{4n^2}{R^2}} \tag{7.115}$$

$$\lambda_{2n} = -\frac{1+i}{2}\varepsilon + \frac{1}{2}\sqrt{(1+i)^2\varepsilon^2 + \frac{4n^2}{R^2}} \tag{7.116}$$

It is seen that λ_{1n} and λ_{2n} are not the negative, the conjugate, or the conjugate of the negative of each other; hence the eight roots are easily obtained from these two independent roots. The homogeneous solution for W_n is written as

$$W_{nH} = \sum_{j=1}^{8} A_{jn}e^{\lambda_{jn}x} \tag{7.117}$$

Similarly,

$$U_{nH} = \sum_{j=1}^{8} B_{jn}e^{\lambda_{jn}x} \tag{7.118}$$

$$V_{nH} = \sum_{j=1}^{8} C_{jn}e^{\lambda_{jn}x}, \tag{7.119}$$

where B_{jn} and C_{jn} are functions of A_{jn} only, because only the particular solutions of Equations (7.107) and (7.108) need be used. Substitution of Equations (7.117) and (7.118) into Equation (7.107) provides the necessary relationship:

$$B_{jn} = A_{jn} \dfrac{-\dfrac{\lambda_{jn}}{R}\left[\dfrac{n^2}{R^2} - \nu\lambda_{jn}^2\right]}{\left[\lambda_{jn}^2 - \dfrac{n^2}{R^2}\right]^2} \qquad (7.120)$$

A similar expression is easily obtained for C_{jn}.

It must be remembered that a particular solution for w must also be obtained for Equation (7.106). This in turn means that the particular solution for w must also be substituted into the right hand side of Equations (7.104) and (7.105).

It is seen that even with the simplified set of equations for cylindrical shells shown here (Donnell equations), under asymmetric loads the computations are generally quite laborious. They are also sensitive, and care should be taken in the solution of any particular problem. For example, it is desirable that whenever higher powers of λ_{jn} appear in the equations, Equations (7.113) and (7.114) be used to reduce the roots so that they appear to the first power.

It should be remembered that the Donnell assumptions can be made for shells of other geometries if they are "shallow."

7.8. INEXTENSIONAL SHELL THEORY

A second simplified shell theory that has utility under some conditions is inextensional shell theory. Its characteristics are most easily seen when dealing with a simple geometry, so it is treated here with regard to a cylindrical shell; but it is obviously not restricted to shells of this geometry.

Inextensional shell theory finds application when (1) the load applied is not axially symmetric and is confined to a small portion of the shell circumferentially, or (2) the lateral pressure oscillates in a manner such that

$$\int_0^{2\pi} p(x,\theta)\, d\theta \approx 0$$

and when the ends of the shell are free to deform.

In these cases the shell resists the load primarily in circumferential bending rather than through in-plane (membrane) action. Consider the two cases in Sketch 7.7, looking at the cross section of a cylindrical shell:

In the first case (a), the load is uniform around the circumference. The original midsurface plane (solid line) is displaced uniformly in a radial

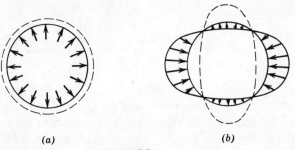

(a)   (b)

Sketch 7.7

direction to the position shown by the dashed line. No bending occurs at all; there has been an extension of the midsurface plane (the neutral axis). This response is called *membrane* action; it will be discussed in the next section.

Conversely, in the second case (b), the sign of the load oscillates around the circumference, so that the shell midsurface plane is deformed into an oval shape, in which there is considerable bending, as seen by the change in the curvature, and no extension of the midsurface circumferential length. Such deformations are therefore described as *inextensional*.

Stated in another way, a shell deforms under a given load in a manner that results in a minimum strain energy. For nonaxially-symmetric loads, bending deformations occur more easily than membrane deformations do.

In inextensional shell theory, midsurface in-plane strains are assumed to be zero.

$$\varepsilon_x^0 = \varepsilon_{x\theta}^0 = \varepsilon_\theta^0 = 0$$

These are the only assumptions. The ramifications are now investigated for a circular cylindrical shell. From circular-shell theory these midsurface strains are as shown below:

$$\varepsilon_x^0 = \frac{\partial u_0}{\partial x} = 0 \tag{7.121}$$

$$\varepsilon_\theta^0 = \frac{1}{R}\left[\frac{\partial v_0}{\partial \theta} + w\right] = 0 \tag{7.122}$$

$$\varepsilon_{x\theta}^0 = \frac{\partial v_0}{\partial x} + \frac{1}{R}\frac{\partial u_0}{\partial \theta} = 0 \tag{7.123}$$

When these are substituted into Equations (7.10) through (7.12), the most important aspects of inextensional shell theory are clearly seen:

$$N_x = N_\theta = N_{x\theta} = 0 \qquad (7.124)$$

Furthermore, from Equation (7.121), u_0 is a function of θ only, and from Equation (7.122),

$$w = -\frac{\partial v_0}{\partial \theta}. \qquad (7.125)$$

To obtain the solution for a complete circular cylindrical shell, the displacements can again be expanded in a Fourier series in the circumferential direction, as in Equation (7.85). For completeness they are written out as follows:

$$u_0 = \sum_{n=1}^{\infty} U_n \cos n\theta + \sum_{m=1}^{\infty} \overline{U}_m \sin m\theta$$

$$v_0 = \sum_{n=1}^{\infty} V_n(x) \sin n\theta + \sum_{m=1}^{\infty} \overline{V}_m(x) \cos m\theta \qquad (7.126)$$

$$w = \sum_{n=1}^{\infty} W_n(x) \cos n\theta + \sum_{m=1}^{\infty} \overline{W}_m(x) \sin m\theta$$

From Equation (7.121) it is seen that U_n and $\overline{U}_m$ are constants. From Equation (7.123), the following relations are found:

$$V_n(x) = \frac{n}{R} U_n x + A_n$$

$$\overline{V}_m(x) = -\frac{m}{R} \overline{U}_m x + B_m \qquad (7.127)$$

where A_n and B_m are constants. Finally, from Equation (7.122),

$$W_n(x) = -nV_n(x) = -n\left(\frac{n}{R} U_n x + A_n\right)$$

$$W_m(x) = m\overline{V}_m(x) = m\left(-\frac{m}{R} \overline{U}_m x + B_m\right) \qquad (7.128)$$

Having the expressions for the displacement relations, we now turn our attention to the stress couples and shear resultants. From Equation (7.128),

$d^2w/\partial x^2 = 0$ (i.e., there is no curvature in the axial direction); therefore, Equations (7.16) and (7.17) are both simplified. Using Equations (7.126) through (7.128), the stress couples can be written explicitly as follows:

$$M_\theta = -\frac{D}{R^2} \sum_{n=1}^{\infty} \left[\frac{n^2}{R} U_n x + nA_n \right] (n^2-1) \cos n\theta$$

$$-\frac{D}{R^2} \sum_{m=1}^{\infty} \left[\frac{m^2}{R} \overline{U}_m x - mB_m \right] (m^2-1) \sin m\theta \tag{7.129}$$

$$M_x = \nu M_\theta \tag{7.130}$$

$$M_{x\theta} = -\frac{(1-\nu)D}{2R^2} \left\{ \sum_{n=1}^{\infty} (2n^2-1)nU_n \sin n\theta - \sum_{m=1}^{\infty} (2m^2-1)m\overline{U}_m \cos m\theta \right\} \tag{7.131}$$

It may be noted that for $m=n=1$, both M_x and M_θ are 0.

The explicit expression for the shear resultants are found by substituting Equations (7.126) through (7.128) into Equations (7.19) and (7.20). The result is

$$Q_x = -\frac{D}{R^3} \sum_{n=1}^{\infty} n^2 \left(n^2 - \frac{1+\nu}{2} \right) U_n \cos n\theta$$

$$+\frac{D}{R^3} \sum_{m=1}^{\infty} m^2 \left(m^2 + \frac{1+\nu}{2} \right) \overline{U}_m \sin m\theta \tag{7.132}$$

$$Q_\theta = \frac{D}{R^3} \sum_{n=1}^{\infty} n^3(n+1) \left(\frac{n}{R} U_n x + A_n \right) \sin n\theta$$

$$+\frac{D}{R^3} \sum_{m=1}^{\infty} m^3(m-1) \left(\frac{m}{R} \overline{U}_m x - B_m \right) \cos m\theta \tag{7.133}$$

Among the force equilibrium equations [Equations (7.3) through (7.5)] the only meaningful one is the last, which for the inextensional theory is written as

$$\frac{\partial Q_x}{\partial x} + \frac{1}{R}\frac{\partial Q_\theta}{\partial \theta} = -p(x,\theta) \tag{7.134}$$

It is obvious that once the displacements have been assumed to be of the form (7.126), the lateral loading needs to be expanded as follows:

$$p(x,\theta) = \sum_{n=1}^{\infty} P_n(x)\cos n\theta + \sum_{m=1}^{\infty} \overline{P}_m(x)\sin m\theta \tag{7.135}$$

where $P_n(x)$ and $\overline{P}_m(x)$ are to be known functions of the axial coordinate. From the form of the preceding equations, the following important relations are found:

$$P_n(x) = -(n+1)\frac{n^4}{R^4}\left[\frac{n}{R}U_n x + A_n\right]$$

$$\overline{P}_m(x) = (m-1)\frac{m^4}{R^4}\left[\frac{m}{R}\overline{U}_m x - B_m\right] \tag{7.136}$$

Two very important conclusions may be deduced from these equations. First, for inextensional shell theory to be applicable, the lateral load $p(x,\theta)$ can at most be a linear function of x. Secondly, since U_n, A_n, $\overline{U}_m$, and B_m are uniquely determined by the applied load; no unknown constants remain. Therefore, in inextensional shell theory no boundary conditions can be satisfied on the ends of the shell (edges where the meridional coordinate is a constant).

As for the first conclusion, if the lateral load is nonlinear but a slowly varying function in x, inextensional shell theory may still be used to obtain an approximate solution. However, in this case it is preferable to utilize an energy principle to obtain an approximate solution, wherein the inextensional assumptions are incorporated in the strain energy expression.

Concerning the second conclusion, for any given problem one must live with the values of deflections, stress couples, and shear resultants resulting on the ends of the shell. It can also be concluded that for a given shell and loading, if the deflections and stresses calculated at the end differ markedly from the actual physical situation, then inextensional shell theory should not be used to obtain a solution. This in turn implies that in that particular case the shell does not deform inextensionally.

7.9. MEMBRANE SHELL THEORY

A third simplified shell theory is called membrane theory. Although it can be applied to shells of any general shape, it is treated here in detail for the case of a cylindrical shell. The fundamental assumption of this theory is that the shell has no bending resistance, that is, that all loads are resisted purely extensionally. It is obvious that membrane theory cannot be rationally used when discontinuities in the lateral loading occur, since it was shown previously that such discontinuities always result in a significant bending boundary layer.

To obtain the governing equations for membrane shell theory, it is sufficient to merely insert the following expression into the governing equations:

$$D = 0 \qquad (7.137)$$

For the case of a circular cylindrical shell, substitution of Equation (7.137) into Equations (7.3) through (7.23) results in the following:

$$M_x = M_\theta = M_{x\theta} = Q_x = Q_\theta = 0$$

For simplicity, in what follows it is assumed that surface shear stresses are zero; hence $q_x = q_\theta = m_x = m_\theta = 0$.

From the third equilibrium equation, Equation (7.5), it is seen that

$$N_\theta = p(x, \theta) R \qquad (7.138)$$

Integration of Equation (7.4) results in

$$N_{x\theta} = N_{\theta x} = - \int \frac{\partial p}{\partial \theta} \, dx + f_1(\theta) \qquad (7.139)$$

where $f_1(\theta)$ is to be determined by the boundary conditions. Likewise, Equation (7.3) can be integrated to yield

$$N_x = - \frac{1}{R} \int \frac{\partial N_{x\theta}}{\partial \theta} \, dx + f_2(\theta) \qquad (7.140)$$

where $f_2(\theta)$ is another function to be specified by the boundary conditions.

Manipulation of Equations (7.10) through (7.12) results in the following convenient form for the displacements in terms of the stress resultants:

$$\frac{\partial u_o}{\partial x} = \frac{1}{Eh}[N_x - \nu N_\theta]$$

$$\frac{1}{R}\frac{\partial v_o}{\partial \theta} + \frac{w}{R} = \frac{1}{Eh}[N_\theta - \nu N_x]$$

$$\frac{1}{R}\frac{\partial u_o}{\partial \theta} + \frac{\partial v_o}{\partial x} = \frac{2(1+\nu)}{Eh}N_{x\theta}$$

Integrating these, expressions for the deflections are found:

$$Ehu_o = \int (N_x - \nu N_\theta)\,dx + f_3(\theta) \tag{7.141}$$

$$Ehv_o = \int 2(1+\nu)N_{x\theta}\,dx - \int \frac{Eh}{R}\frac{\partial u_o}{\partial \theta}\,dx + f_4(\theta) \tag{7.142}$$

$$Ehw = (N_\theta - \nu N_x)R - Eh\frac{\partial v_o}{\partial \theta} \tag{7.143}$$

In the above, $f_3(\theta)$ and $f_4(\theta)$ are also functions to be determined by the boundary conditions.

Thus for a circular cylindrical shell and a given lateral loading $p(x,\theta)$, all stress resultants and displacements are easily found by integrating, in order, Equations (7.138) through (7.143), and subsequently determining the functions f_1 through f_4 so as to satisfy suitable boundary conditions. It should be noted that membrane-theory solutions for shells of other geometries are equally simple to obtain.

Turning to the boundary conditions, it is seen that there are only four to be satisfied. If the cylindrical shell is closed, then two boundary conditions can be satisfied at each end. From Section 7.1 it is obvious that for $x =$ constant edges the natural boundary conditions are

Either u_0 prescribed or $N_x = 0$

Either v_0 prescribed or $N_{x\theta} = 0$

Note that in using membrane theory it is impossible to specify values of the lateral deflection or the slope at the boundaries. The physical implication of this is that bending stresses and deformations are introduced into the shell whenever the boundary conditions involve restraints on lateral deflections or slopes, such as in the case of simply supported or clamped edges. Hence a "bending boundary layer" is introduced.

Membrane theory is widely used (and misused) in the analysis of shells. Because it is so easy to obtain solutions, it is tempting to utilize the theory whenever possible. All too often in design, shell thicknesses are determined on the basis of membrane theory, and as a result the shell is underdesigned, as pointed out in Section 7.5.1. When the shell is composed of ductile materials, local yielding in the region of high bending stresses "hides" the inadequate design. However, in shells that utilize less ductile materials or when allowable stresses are high, the determination of the shell thickness by the misuse of membrane theory (ignoring bending stresses) can lead to catastrophic results.

One of the very important uses of membrane theory is to obtain particular solutions for use in the general theory for shells of any shape. Since in many cases the membrane solution is also a solution to the governing differential equations for the shell, it can be effectively used as the particular solution. This is illustrated in the following section for the case of a cylindrical shell. Whenever a membrane solution is obtained for use as a particular solution, either f_1 through f_4 can be taken as zero, or they can be found through the imposition of the boundary conditions for the problem to which the membrane solution corresponds. The latter alternative is preferable; the former is acceptable.

7.10. EXAMPLES OF MEMBRANE THEORY

7.10.1. Cylindrical Shell with Free Ends, Subjected to a Constant Internal Pressure p_0

The boundary conditions at each end $(x = 0, L)$ are $u_o(0) = N_x(L) = v_o(0) = v(L) = 0$, which results in $f_1 = f_2 = f_3 = f_4 = 0$. From Equations (7.138) through (7.143), the solution is as follows:

$$N_\theta = Rp_0$$

$$N_x = N_{x\theta} = 0$$

$$u_0(x) = -\frac{\nu Rp_0 x}{Eh} = -\frac{\nu p_0 x}{4\varepsilon^4 RD} \qquad (7.144)$$

$$v_0 = 0$$

$$w = \frac{p_0 R^2}{Eh} = \frac{p_0}{4\varepsilon^4 D} \qquad (7.145)$$

Note that the solutions for u_0 and w given in Equations (7.144) and (7.145) are the particular solutions for the case of $p(x)=p_0$, $N_x=0$, found previously in the general shell theory given by Equations (7.48) and (7.52). This illustrates the utility of using membrane solutions as particular solutions. This example is the simplest imaginable case, and membrane theory obviously need not have been employed. However, in more complicated loadings and geometries, the membrane solution used as a particular solution has great advantages when applicable.

7.10.2. Horizontal Cylindrical Shell Filled With a Liquid

Consider the shell shown below, filled with a liquid such that $p(\theta)=p_0 - \gamma R\cos\theta$, where γ is the weight density of the fluid. The shell is clamped at one end and free at the other.

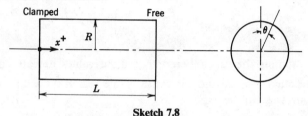

Sketch 7.8

Systematic use of Equations (7.138) through (7.143) results in the complete solution. The boundary conditions are

$$u_o(0) = v_o(0) = N_x(L) = N_{x\theta}(L) = 0$$

The results are as follows:

$$N_\theta = Rp_0 - \gamma R^2 \cos\theta$$

$$N_x = \frac{\gamma}{2}(L-x)^2 \cos\theta$$

$$N_{x\theta} = \gamma R(L-x)\sin\theta$$

$$Ehu_0 = \left[\frac{x^3}{6} + \nu R^2 x - \frac{Lx^2}{2} + \frac{L^2 x}{2} \right] \gamma\cos\theta - \nu R p_0 x$$

$$Ehv_0 = 2\gamma R\sin\theta \left[(1+\nu)\left(-\frac{x^2}{2} + xL \right) + \frac{x^4}{48R^2} + \frac{\nu x^2}{4} - \frac{Lx^3}{12R^2} + \frac{L^2 x^2}{8R^2} \right]$$

$$Ehw = \gamma R \cos\theta \left\{ -R^2 - \nu\left(xL - \frac{L^2}{2}\right) + x^2 - 2xL - \frac{x^4}{24R^2} \right.$$

$$\left. + \frac{x^3 L}{6R^2} - \frac{x^2 L^2}{4R^2} \right\} + p_0 R^2$$

Furthermore, the maximum membrane stresses can be found:

$$\sigma_{x\,max} = \sigma_x\left(0, \begin{array}{c} 0 \\ \pi \end{array}\right) = \pm\frac{\gamma L^2}{2h}$$

$$\sigma_{\theta\,max} = \sigma_\theta(x, \pi) = \frac{p_0 R + \gamma R^2}{h}$$

$$\sigma_{x\theta\,max} = \sigma_{x\theta}\left(0, \begin{array}{c} \pi/2 \\ 3\pi/2 \end{array}\right) = \pm\frac{\gamma RL}{h}$$

However, it must be remembered that these values deviate considerably from the actual total stresses, because in the region $0 \leqslant x \leqslant 4\sqrt{Rh}$ sizable bending stresses can be expected.

7.11 REFERENCES

1. J. R. Vinson, "Edge Load Solutions for Conical Shells," *J. Eng. Mech. Div., ASCE*, **92**, pp. 37–58 (February 1966).

2. ASME Boiler and Pressure Vessel Code, Section III, "Nuclear Pressure Vessels."

3. L. H. Donnell, "Stability of Thin Walled Tubes Under Torsion," NACA Report No. 479, 1933.

4. N. J. Hoff, J. Kempner, and F. V. Pohle, "Line Loads Applied Along Generators of Thin Walled Circular Cylinders of Finite Length," *Q. Appl. Math.*, **11**, 411–426, 1954.

The following is general reference material on the theory of shells, and is not inclusive, but comprises much of the literature in book form, including most of the engineering solutions that are available today in book form.

5. S. P. Timoshenko, and S. Woinowsky-Krieger *Theory of Plates and Shells*, McGraw-Hill, 1959.

6. V. V. Novozhilov, *The Theory of Thin Shells*, Noordhoff, 1959.

7. A. M. Haas, and A. L. Bouma, *Proceedings of the Symposium on Shell Research*, North-Holland, 1961.

8. Kh. M. Mushtari, and K. Z. Galimov, *Non-linear Theory of Thin Elastic Shells*, published for NSF and NASA by the Israel Program for Scientific Translations, 1961 (original in Russian, dated 1957).

9. S. A. Ambartsumyan, *Theory of Anisotropic Shells*, NASA N64-22801, 1964.

10. V. Z. Vlasov, *General Theory of Shells and its Application in Engineering*, NASA TTF-99, N64-19883, 1964.

11. J. E. Gibson, *Linear Elastic Theory of Thin Shells*, Pergamon, 1965.

12. V. Z. Vlasov, and N. N. Leont'ev, *Beams, Plates and Shells on Elastic Foundations*, published for NASA and NSF by the Israel Program for Scientific Translations, 1966 (original in Russian, dated 1960).

13. P. M. Ogibalov, *Dynamics and Strength of Shells*, published for NASA and NSF by the Israel Program for Scientific Translations, 1966 (original in Russian, dated 1963).

14. H. Kraus, *Thin Elastic Shells*, Wiley, 1967.

15. E. H. Baker, A. P. Cappelli, L. Kovalevsky, F. L. Rish, and R. M. Verette, *Shell Analysis Manual*, NASA CR-912 (April 1968).

16. E. H. Baker, L. Kovalevsky, and F. L. Rish, *Structural Analysis of Shells*, McGraw-Hill, 1972.

17. A. W. Leissa, *Vibration of Shells*, NASA SP-288, 1973.

18. J. R. Vinson and T. W. Chou, *Composite Materials and Their Use in Structures*, Applied Science Publishers, 1974.

7.12. PROBLEMS

7.1. A long cylindrical pressure vessel is rated to operate up to 100-psi internal pressure. The wall thickness is 0.1 in. and the mean radius is 50 in. The material is steel with $E = 30 \times 10^6$ psi, $\nu = 0.3$, and $\sigma_{all} = \pm$ 120,000 psi. One end of the cylindrical vessel is considered clamped. Determine σ_x and σ_θ *at the clamped end on the outer surface.*

7.2. A very long steel pipe ($E = 30 \times 10^6$ psi, $\nu = 0.3$, $\sigma_{all} = \pm 30,000$ psi) is to be lifted by using straps located away from either end, tightening up the straps, and subsequently lifting the pipe through hooks attached to the straps. Tightening the straps results in the applied lifting load introducing an axially symmetric radial line load (in pounds per inch of circumference) on the pipe. If the allowable stress is not to be exceeded, what is the maximum value of the line load?

7.3. In the shell problem of Section 7.4, in the bending boundary layer at the simply supported end, $\sigma_{x\,max}$ occurs at $x = \pi/4\varepsilon$. For the same shell, with $\nu = 0.3$, calculate $\sigma_\theta(+h/2)$ and $\sigma_\theta(-h/2)$ at the same location, $x = \pi/4\varepsilon$.

7.4. A lightweight instrument canister to be employed in an orbital research mission consists of a cylindrical shell with ends that are circular plates, assembled so that the junction of the cylinder with the circular plate will continue to be a right angle even under the internal pressures required to prevent electrical arcing. Using the notation of Chapters 4 and 7, what are the boundary conditions at the junction? Use subscripts s for the shell and p for the plates.

7.5. The deep-submergence instrumentation capsule shown in Sketch 7.9 below is designed to provide scientific information at a depth of 1000 ft below the surface of the ocean, where the external pressure is approximately 450 psi. The pressure in the interior of the shell can be considered zero for calculation purposes. The cylindrical shell can be considered as clamped to rigid end plates. The capsule is made of steel ($E = 30 \times 10^6$ psi, $\nu = 0.3$), and is 1 in. thick, 50 in. in radius, and 100 in. long.

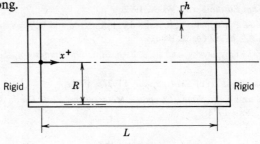

Sketch 7.9

(a) At the end $x = 0$ determine σ_x and σ_θ on both the inside and the outside of the shell.

(b) At the end $x = L$ determine σ_x and σ_θ on both the outside and the inside of the shell. (Think!)

(c) At the midpoint of the shell length ($x = L/2$) determine the values of σ_x and σ_θ.

7.6. The water tower shown in Sketch 7.10 is filled to the top, so that the pressure exerted on the shell walls is given by $p(x) = \rho(L - x)$, where ρ is the weight density of water. The top of the tank ($x = L$) is considered as a free edge, and the bottom of the tank ($x = 0$) is considered to be clamped. The tank height is considerably longer than $4\sqrt{Rh}$.

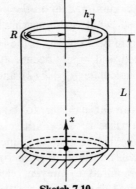

Sketch 7.10

(a) What are the boundary-value constants M_0, Q_0, M_L, and Q_L?

(b) What is the magnitude and location of the maximum value of σ_x? of σ_θ?

(c) What is the magnitude of the deflection at the top of the tank?

7.7. It has been shown that a bending boundary layer occurs when there is a load or geometric discontinuity (such as an edge). It also occurs if there is a material discontinuity or an abrupt change in wall thickness. Consider a vertical column supporting a Texas tower in which one material is used underwater and extending upward to the height of the highest wave predicted, and a second, cheaper material extends from there to the deck (see Sketch 7.11). Thus cylindrical shells of identical geometry but different materials are joined together. If the column is filled with a liquid such as oil or water, so that there is an internal pressure p_i at the joint, (considered constant in the joint area for this calculation), and if the Poisson's ratios of the two materials are equal ($\nu_1 = \nu_2$), what are the values of the stress couple ($M_{L1} = M_{02}$) and the transverse shear resultant ($Q_{L1} = Q_{02}$) at the joint?

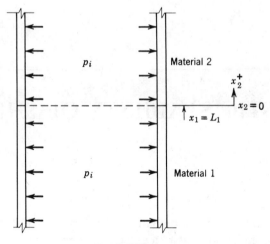

Sketch 7.11

8

ELASTIC STABILITY OF SHELLS

Over and above the determination of stresses and displacements in shell structures, under some loadings the question of the elastic stability of a shell arises, just as it does in plates.

It is beyond the scope of this text either to treat concepts of elastic stability in general, or to provide an encyclopedic, in-depth development of the buckling of shells. Either is the subject of a full-length course or courses. The literature treating shell stability is voluminous. Here, only an introduction is provided. It is intended, however, to provide sufficient treatment of up-to-date methods by which critical loads and stresses can be calculated for some common shell geometries under some common loadings.

8.1. BUCKLING OF ISOTROPIC CIRCULAR CYLINDRICAL SHELLS UNDER AXIALLY SYMMETRIC AXIAL LOADS

Consider the governing differential equation for a circular cylindrical shell under axially symmetric loads, derived in Chapter 7 and given in Equations (7.36) and (7.37):

$$\frac{d^4w}{dx^4} + 4\varepsilon^4 w = \frac{1}{D}\left[p(x) - \frac{\nu N_x}{R} \right] \tag{8.1}$$

where

$$\varepsilon^4 = \frac{3(1-\nu^2)}{h^2 R^2} \tag{8.2}$$

As in the buckling of columns, the axial critical buckling load does not depend upon the lateral distributed loading, $p(x)$. Hence in calculating the critical load here, we may put $p(x)=0$. Thus the solution to Equation (8.1) can be written as

$$w(x) = Ae^{-\varepsilon x}\cos\varepsilon x + Be^{-\varepsilon x}\sin\varepsilon x + Ce^{\varepsilon x}\cos\varepsilon x$$

$$+ Ee^{\varepsilon x}\sin\varepsilon x - \frac{\nu N_x R}{Eh} \tag{8.3}$$

It is therefore seen that independent of the boundary conditions i.e., (where $A = B = C = E = 0$, an unrestrained shell), the load N_x causes a lateral displacement

$$w = -\frac{\nu N_x R}{Eh} \tag{8.4}$$

For the case of buckling, we wish to measure the lateral displacement after the uniform compressive load is applied, not from the unstrained middle surface; hence we define $\bar{w}$ as

$$\bar{w} = w + \frac{\nu N_x R}{Eh} \tag{8.5}$$

The substitution of Equation (8.5) into Equation (8.1) results in

$$\frac{d^4\overline{w}}{dx^4} + 4\varepsilon^4\overline{w} = 0 \tag{8.6}$$

One has thus canceled out the effects of the axial load (below the critical load) on the lateral displacement, and can now see under what loading conditions (if any) other lateral deflections might occur, due to the axial load N_x.

We recall the governing equations for plates, with an in-plane load N_x that causes lateral deflections—for example, Equation (5.3)-and similarly Equation (5.4) for a beam-column. Analogously, one can modify Equation (8.6) to

$$\frac{d^4\overline{w}}{dx^4} + 4\varepsilon^4\overline{w} - \frac{N_x}{D}\frac{d^2\overline{w}}{dx^2} = 0 \tag{8.7}$$

Again, as was done in determining the buckling loads of beam-columns or plates, one can assume the buckled shape (the mode shape or eigenfunction) for a specified set of boundary conditions and solve for the particular load (the critical load or eigenvalue) that will cause buckling in that mode. In this case, if the cylindrical shell is simply supported at both ends, the lateral deflection that will satisfy the boundary conditions is

$$\overline{w}(x) = A\sin\frac{n\pi x}{L} \tag{8.8}$$

Substituting this expression into Equation (8.7) results in

$$\left[\frac{n^4\pi^4}{L^4} + 4\varepsilon^4 + \frac{N_x}{D}\frac{n^2\pi^2}{L^2}\right]A\sin\frac{n\pi x}{L} = 0$$

For this to be true for all x, it is required that

$$N_x = -D\left[\frac{n^2\pi^2}{L^2} + \frac{EhL^2}{DR^2n^2\pi^2}\right] \tag{8.9}$$

This means that if an axial load N_x causes a lateral displacement given by Equation (8.4) ($w = -\nu N_x R/Eh$) then only when the value of axial load attains that given by Equation (8.9) will the additional lateral displacement given by Equation (8.8) occur. As for plates and columns, this latter condition is termed buckling, or elastic instability. For each value of n, there is a unique buckling mode shape and a unique buckling load. As in all continuous elastic bodies, there are an infinity of mode shapes and buckling loads. However, physically speaking, in a specified body with specified boundary conditions, for a given loading condition in which the load increases from zero, when the lowest buckling load is reached, the body buckles and perhaps permanently deforms or fractures. Thus, in studying buckling one usually seeks the lowest buckling load and mode shape for a given loading mechanism, and there is little interest in higher loads and modes. This is one difference between buckling and natural-vibration problems, where one is usually interested in determining a large number of vibration modes (eigenfunctions) and natural frequencies (eigenvalues).

To pursue this example further, let $n = 1$ in Equation (8.9); then

$$N_x = - D \left[\frac{\pi^2}{L^2} + \frac{EhL^2}{DR^2\pi^2} \right]$$

It is seen that N_x is a function of the length of the shell, L, and to find the minimum buckling load N_x, we set the derivative of N_x with respect to L equal to zero. The length at which the minimum buckling load occurs is

$$L = \pi \sqrt[4]{\frac{R^2h^2}{12(1-\nu^2)}} \ , \tag{8.10}$$

and the minimum buckling load is

$$N_{x\,min} = - \frac{Eh^2}{R\sqrt{3(1-\nu^2)}} \tag{8.11}$$

Note that if L is greater or less than the value given by Equation (8.10), the buckling load will be higher for $n = 1$.

Returning to Equation (8.9), letting $n = 2, 3, 4, \ldots$, and following the same procedure, we find in each case that the minimum buckling load equals that given by Equation (8.11). Hence it is conservative to say that for axially symmetric buckling of a simply supported, circular cylindrical, isotropic shell under axial loading,

$$N_{x\,cr} = - \frac{Eh^2}{R\sqrt{3(1-\nu^2)}} \qquad \text{for } L \geqslant \pi \sqrt[4]{\frac{R^2h^2}{12(1-\nu^2)}} \tag{8.12}$$

or

$$\sigma_{x\,cr} = \frac{N_x}{h} = -\frac{Eh}{R\sqrt{3(1-\nu^2)}}$$

In some literature, where $\nu = 0.3$, one often sees the relation written as

$$\sigma_{xcr} = -0.605\frac{Eh}{R} \qquad \text{for } L \geqslant 1.72\sqrt{Rh} \qquad (8.13)$$

In practice these buckling loads cannot be reached. Equations (8.12) and (8.13) represent the critical stress causing buckling, but only in a linear theory. Moreover, although there is a close correlation between theory and experimental data on the elastic and plastic buckling of flat plates under various types of loading and boundary conditions, no such correlation exists in shells under axial compressive loads. This implies that in the cylindrical shells, initial imperfections are very important, and this conclusion has led to a great deal of study during the last decade. The buckling load is particularly important, because under axial compression, buckling is synonymous with collapse of the shell.

Hence it is necessary to incorporate an empirical factor in all equations in order to relate the theoretical values to the actual test data. According to Reference 1, Equation (8.12) is modified to

$$\sigma_{x\,cr} = -\frac{\gamma E}{\sqrt{3(1-\nu^2)}}\frac{h}{R} \qquad (8.14)$$

where in this case,

$$\gamma = 1 - 0.901(1 - e^{-\phi}) \qquad (8.15)$$

where

$$\phi = \frac{1}{16}\sqrt{\frac{R}{h}}$$

The coefficient γ, evaluated by Seide et al.,[2] provides a good lower bound for the majority of existing test data. However, these expressions should not be used for $L/R \geqslant 5$, because of insufficient experimental verification in that range.

Moreover, because of the difficulties in analytically characterizing end restraints other than those of simple support, Equation (8.14) should be used unless there is specific experimental verification for the particular shell geometry and boundary conditions.

In using Equations (8.14) and (8.15) to analyze what the critical stress or critical load is for a shell of specified geometry and material, the procedure is straightforward. However, note that in designing a shell, that is, determining the thickness h for a shell to carry a particular load without buckling, the procedure becomes an iterative one.

Note also that the total load P_{cr} (lb) corresponding to the critical stress σ_{xcr} of Equation (8.14) is

$$P_{cr} = 2\pi R h \sigma_{xcr}$$

8.2. BUCKLING OF ISOTROPIC CIRCULAR CYLINDRICAL SHELLS UNDER AXIALLY SYMMETRIC AXIAL LOADS AND AN INTERNAL PRESSURE

Lo, Crate, and Schwartz[3] studied this problem in some detail. They showed that buckling loads increase as a result of internal pressure. They postulate that the increase is due to the membrane effects of the internal pressure, which reduce the effects of local imperfections in the shell.

Their results can be plotted as in Sketch 8.1, where C is the coefficient in the Equation below, and p is the internal pressure. Thus when $p \geq 0.184E$ $(h/R)^2$, the classical buckling stress of Equation (8.12) or (8.13) is reached. To generalize the results of Lo et al.,[3] calculate the ordinate value from Equations (8.14) and (8.15) to obtain the $p = 0$ value (not necessarily 0.2). Then interpolate linearly between that value and the classical value for an abscissa of 0.184.

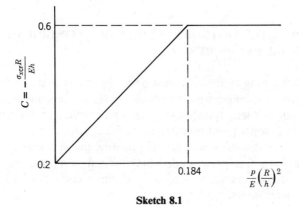

Sketch 8.1

8.3. BUCKLING OF ISOTROPIC CIRCULAR CYLINDRICAL SHELLS UNDER BENDING

The situation is shown in Sketch 8.2. Again, buckling and collapse coincide for isotropic, unpressurized circular cylinders in bending. Equation (8.14) can again be used, but because there is not good agreement between experiment and theory, we use an empirical expression based on the data of Seide et al.[2]:

$$\gamma = 1 - 0.731(1 - e^{-\phi}) \tag{8.16}$$

where

$$\phi = \frac{1}{16}\sqrt{\frac{R}{h}}$$

In this case the buckling stress of Equation (8.14) is related to the overall bending moment by

$$\sigma_x = \frac{MR}{\pi R^3 h} = \frac{M}{\pi R^2 h}$$

where $I = \pi R^3 h$.

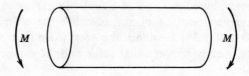

Sketch 8.2

8.4. BUCKLING OF ISOTROPIC CIRCULAR CYLINDRICAL SHELLS UNDER LATERAL PRESSURES

It is found that a long cylindrical shell under lateral or hydrostatic loading buckles into two circumferential harmonic waves in the same manner as a ring. As the cylinder length decreases, the number of circumferential waves increases, with a consequent increase in buckling stress.

For very short cylinders under lateral pressure, the behavior corresponds to that of a long flat plate under longitudinal compression, with the boundary conditions along its longitudinal edges corresponding to those along the cylinder edges.

The buckling behavior of a hydrostatically loaded short cylinder theoretically approaches that of a long flat plate with biaxial compressive loading. In Sketch 8.3, the long edges would have an applied stress of $\sigma = pR/2h$, in addition to the stress shown on the short edge.

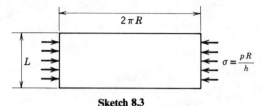

Sketch 8.3

Thus in each of the above cases, the methods of Chapters 5 and 6 can be employed.

For a long shell, defined as one with $\gamma z > 100$, where $z = L^2(1-\nu^2)^{1/2}/Rh$, the critical pressure causing buckling is

$$p_{cr} = \frac{0.926\sqrt{\gamma}\, E}{(R/h)^{5/2}(L/R)} \qquad (8.17)$$

Available experimental data agree reasonably well with the classical buckling theory, but some tests fall as much as 5 percent below theory, as shown by Batdorf.[4] Hence Reference 1 recommends using $\gamma = 0.90$ with Equation (8.17).

8.5. BUCKLING OF ISOTROPIC CIRCULAR CYLINDRICAL SHELLS IN TORSION

The agreement between linear theory and experimental results for the buckling of cylindrical shells in torsion (see Sketch 8.4) is much better than for the same cylinders subjected to axial compression or bending. This means that under torsional loadings initial imperfections are relatively unimportant.

The analytical methods are more complicated than those for axial loads or lateral pressures because the assumed mode shape functions are not products of trigonometric functions. Physically, this means that there are no generators that remain straight during buckling. In torsion the modal lines are helical.

Another difference is that buckling under torsion in the elastic range is not accompanied by immediate collapse. The collapse of an isotropic circular cylinder in torsion occurs at a considerably higher twist angle. However, the collapse load is only slightly higher than the buckling load, which can be used as good approximation for the collapse load. For geometries such that

$$50 < \gamma z < 78(R/h)^2(1-\nu^2) \tag{8.18a}$$

where $z = L^2(1-\nu^2)/Rh$,

$$\sigma_{x\theta\,\mathrm{cr}} = \frac{0.747\gamma^{3/4}E}{(R/h)^{5/4}(L/R)^{1/2}} \tag{8.18b}$$

For $\gamma z > 78(R/h)^2(1-\nu^2)$,

$$\sigma_{x\theta\,\mathrm{cr}} = \frac{\gamma E}{3\sqrt{2}\,(1-\nu^2)^{3/4}}\left(\frac{h}{R}\right)^{3/2} \tag{8.19}$$

In both formulas $\gamma = 0.80$ is recommended in Reference 1 to approximate the lower limit of the bulk of the experimental data. Also, $\sigma_{x\theta}$ is related to an overall torque by

Sketch 8.4

$$T = 2\pi R^2 h\sigma_{x\theta}$$

8.6. BUCKLING OF ISOTROPIC CIRCULAR CYLINDRIC SHELLS UNDER COMBINED AXIAL LOADS AND BENDING LOADS

Since the nature of the buckling patterns is the same for axial compression and bending, a linear interaction curve fits all test data well:

$$R_C + R_B = 1 \tag{8.20}$$

where

$$R_C = \frac{\sigma_x}{\sigma_{x\,\mathrm{cr}}}, \qquad R_B = \frac{\sigma_B}{\sigma_{B\,\mathrm{cr}}}$$

$$\sigma_x = N_x/h$$

$$\sigma_B = \pm MR/\pi R^3 h.$$

In the expression for σ_B use the negative stress value, since buckling will occur on the side where the bending stresses are compressive.

The stress couple M is the total stress couple applied to the shell in a beam-bending situation and is given in in.-lb. The values of $\sigma_{x\,cr}$ and $\sigma_{B\,cr}$ are given by Equation (8.14) with the help of Equations (8.15) and (8.16), respectively.

According to Equation (8.20) the buckling occurs when a combination of applied axial load and bending load increases the sum of the ratios to unity.

8.7. BUCKLING OF ISOTROPIC CIRCULAR CYLINDRICAL SHELLS UNDER COMBINED AXIAL LOAD AND TORSION

In this case, the criterion is

$$R_C + R_T^2 = 1 \tag{8.21}$$

where

$$R_T = \frac{\sigma_{x\theta}}{\sigma_{x\theta\,cr}}, \qquad \sigma_{x\theta} = \frac{T}{2\pi R^2 h}.$$

Here T is the total torque applied to the end of the cylindrical shell, and $\sigma_{x\theta\,cr}$ is given by Equation (8.18) or (8.19).

8.8. BUCKLING OF ISOTROPIC CIRCULAR CYLINDRICAL SHELLS UNDER COMBINED BENDING AND TORSION

Here the interaction equation can be written

$$R_B^{1.5} + R_T^2 = 1 \tag{8.22}$$

where both quantities have been defined previously.

8.9. BUCKLING OF ISOTROPIC CIRCULAR CYLINDRICAL SHELLS UNDER COMBINED BENDING AND TRANSVERSE SHEAR

In this case a shell is subjected to the action of a stress couple M and a transverse shear resultant V, in the manner of a beam, as shown in sketch 8.5 below: The interaction equation is found to be

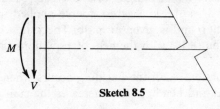

Sketch 8.5

$$R_B + R_s^2 = 1$$

where

$$R_S = \frac{\sigma_{\theta x \, max}}{\sigma_{T \, cr}^*} \qquad (8.23)$$

and

$$\sigma_{x \theta \, max} = V/\pi R h$$

$$\sigma_{T \, cr}^* = 1.25 \sigma_{x \theta \, cr}$$

Here $\sigma_{x \theta \, cr}$ is given by either Equation (8.18) or (8.19).

8.10. BUCKLING OF ISOTROPIC CIRCULAR CYLINDRICAL SHELLS UNDER COMBINED AXIAL COMPRESSION, BENDING, AND TORSION.

Here the interaction equation can be written as

$$R_C + R_B + R_T^2 = 1 \qquad (8.24)$$

This is a tentative relationship to be used until more test data becomes available.

8.11. BUCKLING OF ISOTROPIC SPHERICAL SHELLS UNDER EXTERNAL PRESSURE

Here also, there is much evidence of premature buckling of spherical shells due to imperfect sphericity, and this effect is even more pronounced in spherical shells than in cylindrical shells.

An empirical buckling equation developed at the Naval Ship Research and Development Center provides a conservative estimate of the critical buckling external pressure as

$$p_{cr} = -0.84E\left(\frac{h}{R}\right)^2 \tag{8.25}$$

where of course $\sigma = pR/2h$. This equation is satisfactory whenever initial departures from sphericity are less than $2\frac{1}{2}\%$ of the shell thickness.

8.12. BUCKLING OF ANISOTROPIC AND SANDWICH CYLINDRICAL SHELLS

Pertinent equations for orthotropic cylindrical shells and isotropic sandwich cylindrical shells are found in Reference 1.

The buckling of stiffened cylinders is complicated by the fact that both overall instability and local instability can occur. This is dealt with by Becker.[5]

8.13. REFERENCES

1. *Buckling of Thin-Walled Circular Cylinders.* NASA SP-8007 (September 1965).
2. P. Seide, V. I. Weingarten, and E. J. Morgan, *The Development of Design Criteria for Elastic Stability of Thin Shell Structures*, STL/TR-60-0000-19425 (AFBMO/TR-61-7), Space Technology Laboratory, Inc. (December 31, 1960).
3. H. Lo, H. Crate and E. B. Schwartz, *Buckling of Thin Walled Cylinders Under Axial Compression and Internal Pressure.* NACA TN 1027, 1951.
4. S. B. Batdorf, *A Simplified Method of Elastic Stability Analysis for Thin Cylindrical Shells*, NACA Report 874, 1947.
5. H., Becker, *Handbook of Structural Stability, Part VI, Strength of Stiffened Curved Plates and Shells*, NACA TN 3786, 1958.

8.14. PROBLEMS

8.1. Consider a cylindrical interstage structure on a missile system, of length $L \geqslant 1.72\sqrt{Rh}$, yet with $L/R \leqslant 5$, composed of magnesium ($E = 6.5 \times 10^6$ psi, $\nu = 0.3$, $\sigma_{yield} = \pm 40,000$ psi). If a shell of 30-in. radius and 0.1-in. thickness is subjected to an axial compressive load, what is the critical stress?

8.2. A spherical deep submersible is composed of steel ($E = 30 \times 10^6$ psi, $\sigma_{ult} = 140{,}000$ psi, $\nu = 0.3$), and has an 8-ft diameter and a 0.5-in. wall thickness. If the ocean pressure is given by $p = 0.45d$, where p is in psi and d is in feet, to what depth may the submersible go before buckling occurs? What is the wall stress at the maximum depth?

8.3. A long cylindrical section of a missile, with a 40-in. radius and 1-in. thickness, is subjected to both bending and axial compression during launch (see Sketch 8.6). If the maximum bending moment is 30,000, 000 in.-lb, what axial load can be tolerated without buckling the aluminum shell? ($E = 10 \times 10^6$ psi, $\nu = 0.3$.)

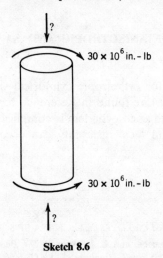

30×10^6 in.- lb

30×10^6 in.- lb

Sketch 8.6

8.4. A long aluminum cylindrical shell support for a water tower ($E = 10 \times 10^6$ psi, $\nu = 0.3$, $\sigma_{all} = 30{,}000$ psi) of 40-in. radius must withstand an axial load of 100,000 lb without buckling. To the nearest hundredth of an inch, what shell thickness is required?

9

SOLUTIONS TO PROBLEMS

In the following, solutions to most of the problems given at the end of each chapter are included as an aid to the instructor and the student. For engineers in practice who study the text individually, the solutions may be especially useful.

CHAPTER 1

1.1.

$$f = \frac{h}{2}\left[\frac{\partial}{\partial x}(\tau_{1x}+\tau_{2x}) + \frac{\partial}{\partial y}(\tau_{1y}+\tau_{2y})\right]$$

$$g = -\frac{1}{1-\nu}\left[2\frac{\partial^2}{\partial y^2}(\tau_{1x}-\tau_{2x}) + (1-\nu)\frac{\partial^2}{\partial x^2}(\tau_{1x}-\tau_{2x})\right]$$

$$+\frac{1+\nu}{1-\nu}\frac{\partial^2}{\partial x\partial y}(\tau_{1y}-\tau_{2y})$$

$$h = \frac{1}{1-\nu}\left[2\frac{\partial^2}{\partial x^2}(\tau_{1y}-\tau_{2y}) + (1-\nu)\frac{\partial^2}{\partial y^2}(\tau_{1y}-\tau_{2y})\right]$$

$$+\frac{1+\nu}{1-\nu}\frac{\partial^2}{\partial x\partial y}(\tau_{1x}-\tau_{2x})$$

CHAPTER 2

2.1.

$$C_1 = -\frac{A_n}{D\lambda_n^4};$$

$$C_2 = -\frac{A_n}{D\lambda_n^3}\frac{[\cosh\lambda_n a - 1 - \lambda_n a]\sinh\lambda_n a + \lambda_n a\cosh\lambda_n a(\cosh\lambda_n a - 1)}{\sinh^2\lambda_n a - (\lambda_n a)^2}$$

$$C_3 = -\frac{C_2}{\lambda_n};$$

$$C_4 = \frac{A_n}{\lambda_n^3 D} \frac{(1-\lambda_n a)\sinh\lambda_n a + (\lambda_n a)\cosh\lambda_n a(\sinh\lambda_n a - 1)}{\sinh^2\lambda_n a - (\lambda_n a)^2}$$

2.3.

$$C_1 = -\frac{A_n}{D\lambda_n^4}; \qquad C_4 = \frac{A_n}{2D\lambda_n^3}$$

$$C_2 = \frac{A_n}{2D\lambda_n^3} \frac{\sinh\lambda_n a + 2\coth\lambda_n a(1-\cosh\lambda_n a)}{\cosh\lambda_n a + \lambda_n a\sinh\lambda_n a - \lambda_n a\cosh\lambda_n a\coth\lambda_n a}$$

$$C_3 = \frac{A_n}{2D\lambda_n^4\sinh\lambda_n a}\left\{\frac{(\lambda_n a)^2 + 2\cosh\lambda_n a(\cosh\lambda_n a - 1) - 2\lambda_n a\sinh\lambda_n a}{\cosh\lambda_n a + \lambda_n a\sinh\lambda_n a - \lambda_n a\cosh\lambda_n a\coth\lambda_n a}\right\}$$

2.5.

$$C_1 = \frac{A_n \nu}{2D\lambda_n^4}\left\{\frac{\dfrac{1+\nu}{1-\nu}\sinh^2\lambda_n a - \dfrac{2}{\nu}\left[\lambda_n a\sinh\lambda_n a + \dfrac{2}{1-\nu}\cosh\lambda_n a\right] + (\lambda_n a)^2}{\dfrac{3+\nu}{2}\sinh^2\lambda_n a + \dfrac{1-\nu}{2}(\lambda_n a)^2 + \dfrac{2}{1-\nu}}\right\}$$

$$C_2 = \frac{A_n \nu}{2D\lambda_n^3}\left\{\frac{(1-\cosh\lambda_n a)(\sinh\lambda_n a - \lambda_n a) + \dfrac{1}{\nu}(\sinh\lambda_n a - \lambda_n a\cosh\lambda_n a)}{\dfrac{3+\nu}{2}\sinh^2\lambda_n a + \dfrac{1-\nu}{2}(\lambda_n a)^2 + \dfrac{2}{1-\nu}}\right\}$$

$$C_3 = \frac{1+\nu}{1-\nu}\frac{A_n \nu}{2D\lambda_n^4}$$

$$\times\left\{\frac{(1-\cosh\lambda_n a)(\sinh\lambda_n a - \lambda_n a) + \dfrac{1}{\nu}(\sinh\lambda_n a - \lambda_n a\cosh\lambda_n a)}{\dfrac{3+\nu}{2}\sinh^2(\lambda_n a) + \dfrac{1-\nu}{2}(\lambda_n a)^2 + \dfrac{2}{1-\nu}}\right\}$$

$$C_4 = \frac{A_n \nu}{2D\lambda_n^3}$$

$$\left\{ \frac{1 - (1+\nu)\sinh^2\lambda_n a - \dfrac{2(1-\nu)}{\nu}\left(\lambda_n a \sinh\lambda_n a + \dfrac{2\cosh\lambda_n a}{1-\nu}\right) + (1-\nu)(\lambda_n a)^2}{(3+\nu)\sinh^2\lambda_n a + (1-\nu)(\lambda_n a)^2 + \dfrac{4}{1-\nu}} \right\}$$

2.6.

$$w_{max} = w\left(\frac{a}{2}, \frac{a}{2}\right) = \frac{p_0 a^4}{4\pi^4 D}$$

$$\sigma_{x\,max} = \sigma_{y\,max} = \sigma_x\left(\frac{a}{2}, \frac{a}{2}, \pm\frac{h}{2}\right) = \sigma_y\left(\frac{a}{2}, \frac{a}{2}, \pm\frac{h}{2}\right) = \pm\frac{3}{2}\frac{p_0 a^2(1+\nu)}{\pi^2 h^2}$$

$$\sigma_{xz}\left(\begin{matrix}0\\a\end{matrix}, \frac{a}{2}, 0\right) = \sigma_{yz}\left(\frac{a}{2}, \begin{matrix}0\\a\end{matrix}, 0\right) = \pm\frac{3p_0 a}{4\pi h}$$

2.7.

$$C_1 = 4.07\times10^{-3}; \qquad C_2 = 0.0485$$

2.8.

$$b = 4.58 \text{ ft}; \qquad w_{max} = 0.1485 \text{ in.}$$

2.9.

$$h = 0.114 \text{ in.}; \qquad w_{max} = 0.077 \text{ in.}$$

2.10.

$$B_{mn}\frac{16p_0}{mn\pi^2}\left[\underset{m,n \text{ odd only}}{} - \frac{8p_1(-1)^n}{mn\pi^2}\right]_{m \text{ odd only}}$$

2.12.

Clamped: $h = 0.332$ in.;   Simple Supported: $h = 0.358$ in.

2.13.

(a) $h = 0.97$ in.; (b) $h = 0.686$ in.; (c) steel; (d) $h = 0.874$ in.

CHAPTER 3

3.1.

$T = 40 + 300z$ °F; $N^* = 800$ lb/in.; $M^* = 20$ in.-lb/in.

3.2.

$T = 10 + 8000z^2$; $N^* = 733$ lb/in.; $M^* = 0$ by symmetry.

3.5.

$T = 60 + 175z + 125z^2$; $N^* = 2467$ lb/in.; $M^* = 93.2$ in.-lb/in.

CHAPTER 4

4.1.

$$w(0) = -\frac{p_1 a^4}{2D}\left[\frac{1}{32} - \frac{1}{75}\right] = -\frac{0.0089 p_1 a^4}{D}$$

4.2.

$$M_r = M_\theta = M$$

4.5.

$$w_{max} = w(0) = -\frac{p_0 a^4}{64D}$$

$$\sigma_{r\,max} = \sigma_r\left(a, \pm\frac{h}{2}\right) = \pm\frac{3}{4}\,\rho h\frac{a^2}{h^2}$$

$$\sigma_{\theta\,max} = \sigma_\theta\left(0, \pm\frac{h}{2}\right) = \mp\frac{3}{8}\,\frac{p_0 a^2}{h^2}\,(1+\nu)$$

4.6.

$$w_{max} = w(0) = -\frac{\rho h a^4}{64D}$$

$$\sigma_{r\,max} = \sigma_r\left(a, \pm\frac{h}{2}\right) = \pm\frac{3}{4}\rho h\frac{a^2}{h^2}$$

$$\sigma_{\theta\,max} = \sigma_\theta\left(a, \pm\frac{h}{2}\right) = \mp\frac{3}{8}\rho h\frac{a^2}{h^2}\,(1+\nu)$$

Note: These are the same answers as in Problem 4.5, where $\rho h = p_0$.

4.7.

$$Q_{r\,max} = Q_r(b) = \frac{p_0(1-s^2)a}{2s} = \frac{p_0(a^2-b^2)}{2b}$$

Yes, one could look at the plate component as a free body and balance vertical forces because of the pressure p_0 and the shear resultant Q_r at $r = b$. In this case, plate theory is not needed.

4.8.

$$h = 0.5 \text{ in.}$$

CHAPTER 5

5.1.

(a) $h = 0.323$ in.
(b) $h = 0.224$ in.
(c) The aluminum plate is lighter by a factor of almost 2.

5.2.

$$N_{x\,cr} = -\frac{2\pi^2 D}{a^2} = -\frac{2\pi^2 D}{b^2}$$

5.3.

$$h = 1.134 \text{ in.}$$

CHAPTER 6

6.1.

(a) $h = 0.506$ in.,
(b) $h = 1.21$ in.

6.2.

(a) $P_{cr} = -\dfrac{12EI}{L^2}$;   yes;   no

(b) Yes;   yes

6.3.

Case I: $w(x,y) = A \sin \dfrac{\pi x}{a}$

Case II: There are at least eight suitable functions.

Case III:

$$w(x,y) = Ay^2\left[1 - \cos\frac{2\pi x}{a}\right]$$

There are at least eight other suitable functions.

6.4.

$$N_{x\,cr} = -D\left[\frac{4\pi^2}{a^2} + \frac{6(1-\nu)}{b^2}\right]$$

Note: The first term is analogous to the result for a clamped-clamped column of unit width; the second term clearly shows the influence of the simply supported side.

6.5.

Zero

6.6.

If $w(x,y) = A[1 - \cos(2\pi x/a)]\sin(\pi y/b)$ is assumed, then

$$N_{x\,cr} = -\frac{4\pi^2 D}{b^2}\left\{\left(\frac{b}{a}\right)^2 + \frac{3}{16}\left(\frac{a}{b}\right)^3 + \frac{1}{2}\left(\frac{a}{b}\right)\right\}$$

6.7.

If $w(x,y) = A[1 - \cos(2\pi x/a)][1 - \cos(2\pi y/b)]$ is assumed, then

$$N_{x\,cr} = -\frac{4\pi^2 D}{b^2}\left[\frac{2}{3} + \left(\frac{a}{b}\right)^2 + \left(\frac{b}{a}\right)^2\right]$$

6.8.

If $w(x) = A[x^3/a^2 - 2x^2/a + x]$ is assumed, then

$$P_{cr} = -\frac{30EI}{a^2}$$

CHAPTER 7

7.1.

$$\sigma_x\left(L, +\frac{h}{2}\right) = -52,000 \text{ psi}$$

$$\sigma_\theta\left(L, +\frac{h}{2}\right) = -15,600 \text{ psi}$$

7.2.

$$H = -148.5 \text{ lb/in.}$$

7.3.

$$\sigma_\theta \left(\frac{\pi}{4\varepsilon}, +\frac{h}{2} \right) = 0.875 \frac{p_0 R}{h} ; \quad \sigma_\theta \left(\frac{\pi}{4\varepsilon}, -\frac{h}{2} \right) = 0.577 \frac{p_0 R}{h}$$

7.4.

$$w_s = u_{0p}; \quad u_{0s} = w_p; \quad \frac{dw_s}{dx} = \frac{dw_p}{dr}; \quad N_{xs} = -Q_{rp};$$

$$Q_{xs}(L) = -N_{rp} \quad [\text{or } Q_{xs}(0) = N_{rp}]; \quad M_{xs} = M_{rp}$$

7.5.

(a),(b)

$$\sigma_x \left(\begin{matrix} 0 \\ L \end{matrix}, +\frac{h}{2} \right) = \quad 23{,}150 \text{ psi}$$

$$\sigma_x \left(\begin{matrix} 0 \\ L \end{matrix}, -\frac{h}{2} \right) = -45{,}650 \text{ psi}$$

$$\sigma_\theta \left(\begin{matrix} 0 \\ L \end{matrix}, +\frac{h}{2} \right) = \quad 6{,}945 \text{ psi}$$

$$\sigma_\theta \left(\begin{matrix} 0 \\ L \end{matrix}, -\frac{h}{2} \right) = -13{,}695 \text{ psi}$$

(c)

$$\sigma_x \left(\frac{L}{2} \right) = -11{,}250 \text{ psi}$$

$$\sigma_\theta \left(\frac{L}{2} \right) = -22{,}500 \text{ psi}$$

7.6.

(a) $$M_0 = \frac{\rho(1-\varepsilon L)}{2\varepsilon^3}; \qquad Q_0 = \frac{\rho(2\varepsilon L-1)}{2\varepsilon^2}; \qquad M_L = Q_L = 0$$

(b) $$\sigma_{x\,max} = \sigma_x\left(0, \pm \frac{h}{2}\right) = \mp \frac{3\rho(\varepsilon L-1)}{h^2\varepsilon^3}$$

(c) $$w(L) = 0$$

7.7.

$$M_{L_1} = M_{02} = \frac{p_i}{4\varepsilon^2} \frac{(D_1-D_2)^2}{(D_1+D_2)^2 - \frac{1}{2}(D_1-D_2)^2}$$

$$Q_{L_1} = Q_{02} = -\frac{p_i}{2\varepsilon} \frac{(D_1-D_2)^2}{(D_1+D_2)^2 - \frac{1}{2}(D_1-D_2)^2}$$

Note that if $E_1 = E_2$, then $D_1 = D_2$, and these expressions go to zero as one would expect.

CHAPTER 8

8.3.

$$P = 25.5 \times 10^6 \text{ lb}$$

8.4.

$$h = 0.09 \text{ in.}$$

INDEX